P9-AOP-901

THE CAPACITY
DECISION SYSTEM

THE IRWIN SERIES IN
OPERATIONS MANAGEMENT

EDITOR
HOWARD L. TIMMS
Indiana University

THE CAPACITY
DECISION SYSTEM

WILLIAM T. MORRIS
Professor of Industrial Engineering
The Ohio State University

1967
RICHARD D. IRWIN, INC.
Homewood, Illinois

© RICHARD D. IRWIN, INC., 1967

All rights reserved.
This book or any part thereof may not be reproduced
without the written permission of the publisher.

First Printing, April, 1967

Library of Congress Catalog Card No. 67–15839

Printed in the United States of America

HD
39
M57

PREFACE

THIS BOOK attempts to introduce the reader to a broad view of the systems by means of which firms carry out the capital investment function. It begins with the traditional analysis for evaluating the futurity of cash flows and follows this with an introduction to modern utility theory as a means of evaluating the uncertainty of future cash flows. It then moves from the analysis of individual investment proposals to the problem of selecting an investment program from among a number of proposals. Finally, it considers the management systems used to carry on capital budgeting in a firm, emphasizing the problems of delegation and coordination.

Nearly all of the analysis is readily accessible to the reader familiar with algebra and the elements of probability theory.

February, 1967   WILLIAM T. MORRIS

TABLE OF CONTENTS

Chapter 1

BASIC CONCEPTS IN

INVESTMENT DECISIONS

Long-Range Planning, Financial Planning, and Capital Budgeting

THE DECISION SYSTEMS considered in this book appear in the context of the firm's long-range plans for corporate development, its intermediate-range plans for financing this development, and the opportunities for investment which are currently available to it.[1] We are concerned basically with the management decision and information systems which allocate the funds coming into the firm, both from retained earnings and from the money markets, to the investment opportunities which it discovers and creates. These information and decision systems are typically called capital budgeting systems. To appreciate the context in which capital budgeting systems operate one might imagine them as being at the confluence of a stream of information or proposals for investment opportunities and a stream of funds which may be used for some of these opportunities.

Out of the firm's long-range studies of markets, technological development possibilities, and competitive prospects, come the long-range plans outlining corporate grand strategy for growth. These plans in turn lead to policies for research and development of new products and processes; they promote the search for acquisition and merger proposals, and they encourage the discovery of new markets to be penetrated and old markets to be expanded.[2] Out of these activities arises a flow of investment

[1]For an explanation of this total decision system, see Howard L. Timms, *Introduction to Operations Management* (Irwin Series in Operations Management [Homewood, Ill., Richard D. Irwin, Inc., 1967]), chap. 5.

[2]For an explanation of the total system by which ideas for new research and development (product) projects evolve from sociological and technological develop-

1

proposals which are essentially opportunities to change the capacity of the firm, either expanding the output capability for existing lines or entering new and diversified product lines. As these proposals mature and develop, they eventually reach the point at which a decision may be made as to which of them are to be undertaken. Meanwhile, the operating divisions of the firm are also generating a stream of proposals for the replacement of existing facilities with more modern equipment, and the investment in new processes in order to cut production costs. All of these proposals become competitors for the funds which the firm will have available to invest in the near term. Funds which may be placed in these opportunities are also becoming available to the firm. From time to time the financial planning system leads the firm into the capital markets for new equity or debt capital. More or less continuously, the operations of the firm throw off cash in the form of retained earnings and depreciation charges. The capital budgeting problem is thus essentially that of deciding how currently available funds are to be allocated among currently available opportunities. Of course, some of these current opportunities are designed to preserve the liquidity of the funds for future investment in plant capacity. We will be concerned largely with the short-range or near-term decisions, although these are, of course, deeply influenced by the long-range strategy of the firm.

Basic Problems in Cash Flow Evaluation

An investment decision involves an outlay of funds which the firm does not expect to recover during the current year or accounting period. The investment outlay will be recovered over several future years it is hoped, and if the project is successful, something more will be recovered as well. That is, a successful investment is profitable in the sense that the original funds are recovered as well as some "return" in addition. Evaluation of an investment thus requires the prediction of all the incomes and outlays over its useful life. This typically means that predictions of operating costs, sales revenues, maintenance costs, and so on must be made for several years into the future. This necessity for evaluating an investment in terms of its consequences for the extended future raises two basic problems. These cash flows occur at various points in time and their predicted amounts are subject to various degrees of uncertainty. Comparison of two investments requires an evaluation of the "futurity" and the uncertainty of their respective cash flows.

It is clear that a firm, having just installed a new piece of equipment,

---

ments resulting in new market expectations, see Lewis N. Goslin, *The Product Planning System* (Irwin Series in Operations Management [Homewood, Ill., Richard D. Irwin, Inc., 1967]), chap. 1.

would prefer to wait a year before paying for it if given the choice. By postponing payment, the firm could invest the money (or reduce its debt) and thus be richer at the end of the year by the amount earned (or saved) on the investment. More formally, by postponing payment or delaying cash outlays, the firm can increase its net worth at some point in the future.

Thus the firm is interested in the cash inflows and outflows resulting from an investment and in the timing of these flows. For a firm that wishes to maximize its future net worth and has opportunities to invest (or repay) cash, it will always be desirable to postpone a cash outlay. The problem becomes a little more complex if it is offered a chance of paying $85,000 for the equipment now or $100,000 one year hence. Thus some analysis may be useful in evaluating the futurity of cash flows.

The second basic problem arises from the fact that all future events are matters of more or less uncertainty. One cannot be certain of such statements as, "The salvage value of this machine ten years from now will be $20,000." The more data and the more experience which go into such a prediction the more certain it will be, yet some uncertainty always remains. The uncertainty associated with cash flow predictions may differ greatly from one investment to another. To modernize a plant producing a well-established product which has been experiencing a long-term steady growth in demand may be an investment whose consequences are matters of relatively low uncertainty. Yet to build a new plant, using a new process to produce a new product, may involve considerably greater uncertainty. Management will clearly wish to consider this difference in comparing the two investments. Here again some analysis may be useful in evaluating uncertainties in complex situations.

Uncertainty may, of course, be correlated with futurity. The further into the future an event, the greater the uncertainty which surrounds it. For purposes of explanation, however, it is helpful to deal with the two problems separately at first. In this chapter the problem of futurity is discussed, while uncertainty is examined in the following one. The logic of compound interest provides the basis for comparing the futurity of alternative cash flow patterns.

Interest

Calculations involving interest have become a traditional part of the analysis of investment decision problems. The particular interest rate used and the way in which it is used derive directly from considerations of the firm within which the decision is made. There are a variety of situations which lead to the use of interest in the analysis of these problems.

The Cost of Borrowed Funds. Interest considerations first found their way into the analysis of management actions in the days of active railroad construction. Much of the railroads' money came from bonds, and thus it was natural in comparing alternative projects to include the cost of the money that would have to be invested in them. Many firms continue to obtain some part of their funds by means of bonds or loans, as opposed to equity capital. Thus, if one is considering the purchase of a plant which is to be financed by a mortgage, interest charges on the loan will be relevant in comparing the cost of alternative plants. Typically, such a mortgage contract might specify that the lender makes a loan of, say, $100,000 to be secured by the plant itself. This is to be paid back in 20 equal annual payments, with interest on the unpaid balance at 5 percent compounded annually. This means that each year the firm must pay $8,024, some of which reduces the amount of the loan and the remainder of which pays the interest on the amount owed during the year.

The Opportunity Cost of Investments Forgone. Suppose the firm always has available certain investment opportunities. It may, for example, be able to invest funds in its own operations for improvement or expansion, and perhaps money thus invested earns a return of 10 percent. Alternatively, the firm may be able to invest in stocks or bonds, loans to its customers, and so forth. Such a possibility is often called a standard investment opportunity. The firm may then wish to establish the following kind of policy: "Since we can always obtain a return of X percent from our standard investment opportunity, we will not put money in any project unless it will earn at least X percent." Thus, in computing the cost of various alternatives, the analyst may simply add on X percent of the amount invested. Such a cost may be thought of as the opportunity cost of not investing the funds in the standard investment opportunity.

This leads also to the interesting idea of the "time value of money." Since receipts and disbursements resulting from a particular project may occur at various points in time, the question arises, "Is an income of $1 today equivalent to an income of $1 at the end of a year from today?" Clearly, if the firm receives $1 today, it will immediately invest the $1 in the standard investment opportunity, or some other project yielding the same or greater return. Thus, at the end of the year the firm will have the equivalent of $1 plus X percent of $1. Thus a "present dollar" is worth more than a "future dollar," and the relationship between the two depends on the interest rate. If the firm uses an interest rate of 5 percent compounded annually, then $1 today is "equivalent" in the time value sense to

$1.05 at the end of 1 year
$1.103 at the end of 2 years
$1.158 at the end of 3 years

$1.629 at the end of 10 years
$2.653 at the end of 20 years
and so on.

This means that the cost of a project will depend not only on the incomes and outlays involved, but also on the times at which these occur and the interest rate used by the firm.

Satisfactory Return. Another situation closely related to the standard investment opportunity arises when the firm simply establishes a policy that any project which it undertakes must yield at least a certain rate of return. This rate of return it takes to be a satisfactory return or a "minimum attractive return." The only reason for distinguishing this situation is that such a policy may be used even if the standard investment opportunity is not in fact available. Thus the firm may decide that, for the purpose of examining alternative courses of action, it will simply rule out all alternatives which do not result in at least the satisfactory rate of return. Here again, the analyst looking for the least-cost alternative may simply add on a return at the satisfactory rate to the costs of each alternative before choosing.

The Logic of Interest Calculations

Consider an investment of an amount of money in a project which will earn a return of interest on the investment. Say $100 is invested in a project which earns 5 percent each year. If the interest is not withdrawn but is reinvested in the project, then the amount of the investment increases from year to year. If the interest rate remains fixed, the dollar amount of the interest received will also increase, and we have the process of compounding, or compound interest. The history of such an investment is illustrated as follows:

Year	Interest Earned during Year	Amount of Investment at Year End
1.............	$5.00	$105.00
2.............	5.25	110.25
3.............	5.5125	115.7625
4.............	5.7881	121.5506
and so on		

In more general terms let:

P = a sum of money at the present time
S = a sum of money at the end of n periods in the future
i = interest rate expressed as a decimal

The foregoing table may then be expressed by the function

$$S = (1 + i)^n P$$

If, for example, we are interested in the value of the investment at the end of 10 years, the factor $(1 + .05)^{10}$ may be obtained from the interest tables.

$$(1 + .05)^{10} = 1.629$$
$$P = \$100$$
$$S = (1.629)(\$100) = \$162.90$$

Thus, an investment of $100 at 5 percent compound interest will yield the sum of $162.90 at the end of 10 years.

We can also compute the amount which would have to be invested at the present time in order to yield a future sum of a given amount.

$$P = \frac{1}{(1 + i)^n} S$$

The present sum which is "equivalent" in this sense to a given S, is called the present worth of S. A future sum which is equivalent to a given present sum P, is called the future worth of P.

Next consider an investment which will result in a series of n end-of-period payments, each of an equal amount, R. What is such an investment worth in dollars paid today or what is its present worth? We could compute the present worth of each of the equal, end-of-period payments, and then add the present worths.

$$P = \frac{1}{1 + i}R + \frac{1}{(1 + i)^2}R + \frac{1}{(1 + i)^3}R + \frac{1}{(1 + i)^4}R + \cdots$$
$$+ \frac{1}{(1 + i)^n}R$$

The right-hand side of this equation represents the first n terms of a geometric series. It will be recalled that if the nth term of such a series is of the form ar^{n-1}, the sum of the first n terms is given by

$$a\left(\frac{r^n - 1}{r - 1}\right)$$

Using this result we obtain

$$P = \frac{(1 + i)^n - 1}{i(1 + i)^n}R$$

This amount invested now at interest rate i would be sufficient to yield a series of n end-of-period payments each of amount R.

Having found the present worth of such a series of payments, this may easily be transformed into a future worth using the relation already developed between P and S. This gives

$$S = \frac{(1 + i)^n - 1}{i}R$$

This is the amount which will be accumulated at the end of n years if we pay an amount R into a fund each year and the fund earns interest at rate i. For example, suppose a firm contributes \$10,000 annually to its employees' retirement fund, and the fund is kept fully invested at 4 percent. What will be the value of the fund after 20 years? The interest tables give

$$\frac{(1 + .04)^{20} - 1}{.04} = 29.778$$

Thus

$$S = (29.778)(\$10,000) = \$297,780$$

The interest tables found on pages 111–21 give numerical values for the six factors which relate the three variables P, S, and R.

Interest for Periods Other than One Year

In some problems it is necessary to deal with interest which is compounded more frequently than once each year. Suppose, for example, interest is compounded k times per year at a rate of I per period. We may be interested in what annual rate of interest i would be equivalent to compounding k times each year at a rate I. If we were to deposit \$1 in a bank which compounded in this latter way, at the end of one year the dollar would have grown to an amount

$$S = (\$1)(1 + I)^k$$

If we then subtract the original dollar, the remainder will be the interest earned in a year on \$1, or the annual rate of interest expressed as a decimal:

$$(\$1)(1 + I)^k - \$1 = i$$

If, for example, interest is compounded monthly at a rate of 1 percent per month, the annual interest rate equivalent to this is

$$i = (1 + .01)^{12} - 1$$
$$= 1.127 - 1 = .127 \text{ or } 12.7 \text{ percent per year}$$

Machine Selection

An interesting and extensively studied decision problem is that of the choice among machines or other major investments. Typically, the alternatives are assets which will render equal service to the firm.[3] The revenue

---

[3] In selecting between alternative machines where the service level of each alternative depends upon its use as part of a work system, preliminary designs of the alternative work systems must be made; see Gerald Nadler, *Work Systems Design: The Ideals Concept* (Irwin Series in Operations Management [Homewood, Ill.,

of the firm is taken to be independent of the choice, and thus the principle of choice is: *Since the assets are assumed to be equal in all other respects, select that one which minimizes cost.* In principle this is a very simple type of decision, and most of the difficulties encountered are in deciding what costs are to be included and how they are to be predicted.

Consider the specific example of the choice between two machines, *A* and *B*, which are expected to render equal service in a specific application. The relevant outcomes which must be predicted usually include direct and indirect labor, materials, power, fuel, lubricants, replacement parts, maintenance effort, and so forth that will be required to operate each machine. The service life of each and its condition at the end of its service life must also be predicted. In evaluating the outcomes, one uses the initial cost quoted by the seller, the operating expenses which must be estimated, and the salvage value at the end of the service life, which must also be estimated. With this information in hand the analysis simply requires an adding up of the costs and the selection of the minimum cost asset. For example:

	Machine A	Machine B
Initial cost	$20,000	$30,000
Annual operating cost	$ 4,000	$ 3,500
Service life	10 years	10 years
Salvage value	$ 2,000	$ 4,000

The total cost for 10 years' service may easily be computed.

$$\text{Machine } A \ldots\ldots\ldots\ldots \$58,000$$
$$\text{Machine } B \ldots\ldots\ldots\ldots \$61,000$$

The recommendation might then be in favor of machine *A*, and the analysis would be submitted to management review to ascertain if important considerations should be added.

Interest

If interest is to be included in the analysis for one or more of the reasons discussed above, the problem requires some additional calculations. The differing initial investments in the two machines in the previous example and the differing patterns of expense and income over time will be reflected in the interest costs associated with each. To show this, consider a decision in which there are three alternative machines, all of which render equal service in the application anticipated.

The following cost data are given:

Richard D. Irwin, Inc., 1967]), and machine requirements (number of each alternative machine) must be determined. For an explanation of machine requirements see Ruddell Reed, Jr., *Plant Location, Layout, and Maintenance* (Irwin Series in Operations Management [Homewood, Ill., Richard D. Irwin, Inc., 1967]), chap. 5.

	Machine A	Machine B	Machine C
Initial cost	$28,000	$32,000	$35,000
Service life	Five years for all machines		
Operating costs			
Year 1	$ 2,500	$ 2,200	$ 2,000
Year 2	2,500	2,200	2,000
Year 3	2,600	2,200	2,000
Year 4	2,800	2,300	2,000
Year 5	3,000	2,400	2,000
Salvage value	$ 3,000	$ 3,500	$ 4,100

Interest is taken to be 5 percent.

To simplify the analysis, it is usually assumed that the operating costs are to be considered as lump sum expenses occurring at the end of the year in question. Two principles of choice for such a decision will be suggested, although there are a variety of principles available.

① *Assuming the alternatives are equal in all other respects, select the one which minimizes the present worth of the costs incurred.*

②. *Assuming that the alternatives are equal in all other respects, select the one which minimizes the equivalent annual cost.*

As we will show, either of these principles may be used if the assets being compared have equal service lives. If assets having differing service lives are compared, the equivalent annual cost principle is to be used.

Investment Recovery and Interest

In applying either of these principles the analyst must first predict the pattern of costs in time over the life of each asset. Once this has been done, the costs may be converted into an equivalent present worth or an equivalent annual cost. When dealing with productive assets it is common to view the investment as giving rise to two kinds of costs. The first of these is the cost of recovering the investment itself. Once an asset has been purchased, a depreciation policy is established which in effect determines what portion of the investment is to be "charged off" against current revenue at various points during the life. This choice of depreciation policy is equivalent to establishing a pattern of costs for investment recovery over time. There are several depreciation policies in common use. The second cost which arises out of the investment is the cost of interest on the unrecovered portion of the investment. We shall refer to these two costs as investment recovery and interest costs.

From the analyst's viewpoint, it can be shown that it makes no difference what pattern of investment recovery costs over time he predicts as long as his prediction of service life is correct. More specifically, using either of the two principles of choice mentioned previously, the results of all predicted patterns of investment recovery cost will be the same. To show this, suppose we wish to consider an asset in which the initial investment is I, and interest costs are to be taken at $i(100)$ percent. Let

$$x_k = \text{the amount of investment recovery cost at}$$
$$\text{the end of year } k(k = 1, 2, \ldots, n)$$

$$\sum_{k=1}^{n} x_k = I$$

$$i \sum_{j=k}^{n} x_j = \text{interest cost for unrecovered portion of the}$$
$$\text{investment during year } k$$

The present worth of the interest costs plus the investment recovery costs over the life, n, of the asset can be computed as follows:

$$\sum_{k=1}^{n} \left\{ x_k + i \sum_{j=k}^{n} x_j \right\} \frac{1}{(1 + i)^k}$$

This can be expanded and rewritten as:

$$\frac{1 + i}{1 + i} x_1 + \frac{i}{1 + i} x_2 + \frac{1 + i}{(1 + i)^2} x_2 + \frac{i}{1 + i} x_3 + \frac{i}{(1 + i)^2} x_3 + \frac{i}{(1 + i)^3} x_3$$

$$+ \frac{i}{1 + i} x_4 + \cdots\cdots\cdots + \frac{i}{(1 + i)^n} x_n$$

This series then reduces to

$$x_1 + x_2 + \cdots + x_n = \sum_{k=1}^{n} x_n = I$$

Thus we have the result that the present worth of the investment recovery costs plus the interest costs for any pattern over time is simply equal to the initial investment itself. Since the equivalent annual cost of investment recovery plus interest could be computed directly from the present worth just obtained, the result holds also for the second principle of choice. To use this result, the analyst must be willing to assume that the asset will actually serve out its useful life, and will not be retired or replaced prior to this time.

If salvage values are to be taken into consideration, then the foregoing analysis may be modified as follows. Let

$$S_n = \text{salvage value of the asset at the end}$$
$$\text{of } n \text{ years of service}$$

$$\sum_{k=1}^{n} x_k + S_n = I$$

The present worth of interest costs plus investment recovery costs now becomes

$$\sum_{k=1}^{n}\left\{x_k + i\left(S_n + \sum_{j=k}^{n}x_j\right)\right\}\frac{1}{(1+i)^k}$$

which reduces to

$$\sum_{k=1}^{n}x_k + \left(1 - \frac{1}{(1+i)^n}\right)S_n = I - \frac{1}{(1+i)^n}S_n$$

If salvage values are included, the present worth of the sum of investment recovery plus interest costs, for any pattern over time, turns out to be the original investment less the present worth of the salvage value.

The Present Worth Principle

Applying the foregoing result to the example yields the following analysis:

Present Worth of	Machine A	Machine B	Machine C
Investment recovery and interest cost	$25,649.50	$29,257.75	$31,787.65
Operating costs			
Year 1	2,381.00	2,095.28	1,904.80
Year 2	2,267.50	1,995.40	1,814.00
Year 3	2,245.88	1,900.36	1,727.60
Year 4	2,303.56	1,892.21	1,645.40
Year 5	2,350.50	1,880.40	1,567.00
Total present worth	$37,197.94	$39,021.40	$40,446.45

$\left|- \frac{1}{(1+i)^n}S_n\right.$

The present worth of investment recovery and interest costs is found by subtracting the present worth of the salvage value from the original investment. In the case of machine A, for example:

$$\$28,000 - \left\{\frac{1}{(1.05)^5}\right\}\$3,000 = \$25,649.50$$

This analysis would thus lead to the selection of machine A. This selection is conditioned by the assumptions that the machines are equal in all other respects, that interest is to be taken at 5 percent, and that any of the alternatives would serve out its predicted useful life.

The Equivalent Annual Cost Principle

Perhaps the most widely used of the foregoing principles is the second, which suggests the use of equivalent annual cost as a criterion. It has already been shown that the present worth of investment recovery plus interest costs is simply the original investment minus the present worth of the salvage value. The equivalent annual cost of investment recovery plus interest can be easily found by converting this present worth to an equivalent series of equal end-of-period payments.

Equivalent annual cost of investment recovery and interest
$$= \left\{ I - \frac{1}{(1 + i)^n} S_n \right\} \frac{i(1 + i)^n}{(1 + i)^n - 1}$$

$$= (I - S_n) \frac{i(1 + i)^n}{(1 + i)^n - 1} + \left\{ S_n - \frac{S_n}{(1 + i)^n} \right\} \frac{i(1 + i)^n}{(1 + i)^n - 1}$$

$$= (I - S_n) \frac{i(1 + i)_n}{(1 + i)^n - 1} + iS_n$$

This final expression is the one most often used to calculate the equivalent annual cost of investment recovery and interest. This computation applied to machine A in the example yields:

$$\$25,000.00 \ (.23097) + (.05) \ \$3,000.00 = \$5,924.25$$

The operating costs for each machine may be first converted to a present worth, and then to an equivalent annual cost. The comparison of the three machines then looks as follows:

	Machine A	Machine B	Machine C
Equivalent annual cost of investment recovery and interest	$5,924.25	$6,757.64	$7,341.97
Equivalent annual cost of operation	2,667.36	2,255.13	2,000.00
Total equivalent annual cost	8,591.61	9,012.77	9,341.97

Again the choice would be machine A. It should be clear also that these two principles of choice are equivalent. They are related by the expression

$$P \frac{i(1 + i)^n}{(1 + i)^n - 1} = R$$

where P is the present worth and R is the equivalent annual cost. In the case of machine A, for example

$$P = \$37,197.94$$
$$R = \$8,591.61$$
$$\frac{i(1 + i)^n}{(1 + i)^n - 1} = .23097$$

The following equality indicates the equivalence:

$$(\$37,197.94)(.23097) = \$8,591.60$$

(Rounding in the interest tables introduces some inconsequential discrepancies.) Thus we may conclude that when we are choosing among machines having equal service lives, the equivalent annual costs will differ from the present worths only by multiplication by a constant. This any recommendation based upon the present worth principle will be supported as well by the equivalent annual cost principle. We may then formulate the general rule: *When choosing among assets having equal service lives either the present worth principle or the equivalent annual cost principle may be used.* Note that if the service lives of the assets in a decision are different, then the two principles are not equivalent in general. We consider this situation next.

The Major Assumption

Each of the two principles of choice suggested for decisions involving assets contained the assumption that the alternatives were equal in all respects except cost. If this assumption does not hold, then an attempt must be made to express other differences in terms of costs. If this attempt fails, then these other differences must be brought into the decision by some judgmental process. Some typical differences which can be more or less successfully reduced to cost terms will be discussed here.

It is often the case in comparing productive assets that one will have a greater output capacity than another. If the firm can utilize only a fixed level of capacity which is within the capabilities of all the alternatives, then this excess capacity is of no value and can be overlooked. If, however, the firm can utilize the excess capacity, then it must be evaluated and made a part of the analysis. This usually requires the use of a profit maximization principle of choice rather than cost minimization principles.

It often happens also that assets being compared have different potential service lives. There are at least two ways of handling such a difference:

1. If the company requires the service of the asset selected for some given length of time only, then service lives beyond this are of no consequence, except as they reflect upon salvage values. Sometimes the analyst may be uncertain as to the exact length of time the services of the selected asset will be required, and he will define a length of time called a planning period. The length of the planning period is essentially arbitrary but might well represent the best available estimate of the duration of the project. Having assumed a planning period, the analyst neglects service lives beyond it.

2. If the services of the selected asset are assumed to be required indefinitely, then the analyst may assume that in comparing alternatives he is really comparing indefinite sequences of identical assets. That is, each machine will be replaced with an identical successor at the end of its service life, and this process will go on indefinitely (or to a point where all alternatives are replaced at the same time). When this assumption is made, the annual cost principle of choice is especially applicable.

Suppose, for example, we face a decision between two assets described below:

	Machine A	Machine B
Investment	$10,000	$20,000
Service life	5 years	10 years

Assume that neither machine has a salvage value nor involves any operating costs. Clearly it makes little sense to compute the present worths since these are $10,000 and $20,000 for A and B respectively, whatever the rate of interest. These numbers fail to reflect that we are considering 5 years of service in one case and 10 years in the other. We might, however, compare two machines of type A in sequence, with one machine of type B. Thus we would be considering 10 years of service in both cases. If the interest rate is 10 percent then we obtain

Present worth of two A's = $10,000 + (10,000)(.6209) = $16,209
Present worth of one B = $20,000

Thus A appears to be the preferred type. Since 10 years are involved in each case, we can convert these present worths to equivalent annual costs by multiplying by the appropriate constant:

Equivalent annual cost of two A's = (16,209)(.16275) = $2,638
Equivalent annual cost of one B = (20,000)(.16275) = $3,255

What would have happened if we had simply computed the equivalent annual cost for one A and compared it with the equivalent annual cost for one B?

Equivalent annual cost for one A = (10,000)(.26380) = $2,638
Equivalent annual cost for one B = (20,000)(.16275) = $3,255

The results are as before. We may thus conclude that the equivalent annual cost for two identical machines in sequence is equal to that for one such machine. In using the equivalent annual cost principle in this case, we get results which are the same as those arising from a comparison of 10 years of service from two A's with 10 years of service from one B.

This result may be generalized to any number of identical machines in sequence. As before, consider a type of machine which requires an investment I, has service life n, but involves neither salvage value nor operating costs. The present worth of k such machines in sequence may be written

$$I\left\{1 + \frac{1}{(1+i)^n} + \frac{1}{(1+i)^{2n}} + \cdots + \frac{1}{(1+i)^{(k-1)n}}\right\}$$

This is the sum of the first k terms of a geometric series which may be expressed as

$$I\frac{1 - \dfrac{1}{(1+i)^{kn}}}{1 - \dfrac{1}{(1+i)^n}} = I\frac{\{1 - (1+i)^{kn}\}\{1+i\}^n}{\{1 - (1+i)^n\}\{1+i\}^{kn}}$$

To convert this present worth to an equivalent annual cost, multiply by the factor

$$\frac{i(1 + i)^{kn}}{(1 + i)^{kn} - 1}$$

The result is

$$I\frac{i(1 + i)^{n}}{(1 + i)^{n} - 1}$$

which is simply the equivalent annual cost of one machine. The reader may wish to verify that a similar result holds for an infinite sequence of identical machines. This leads us to a second general rule: *In decisions involving assets of different service lives, the equivalent annual cost principle should be used.*

When machines differ with respect to reliability it is sometimes possible to evaluate these differences in terms of maintenance costs, costs of stocking spare parts, and costs of production lost while maintenance was performed. If machines differ with respect to the quality of output, again it may be possible to evaluate scrap and inspection costs and thus measure the differences. Differences in such attributes as safety for the operator begin to be very difficult to evaluate in terms of costs, and must be considered in other ways.

Rate of Return

Suppose one considers a project involving an initial investment and a stream of subsequent incomes and outlays. The present worth of these cash flows might be computed using various interest rates, and it is usually the case that there is an interest rate which will make the present worth equal to zero. This particular interest rate is called the rate of return on the project. In other words, the rate of return is the interest rate which makes the present worth of the cash outflows for a project equal to the present worth of the cash inflows. While some firms find rate of return a useful indicator of investment worth, it should be carefully noted that selecting among alternative investments so as to maximize the rate of return will not *necessarily* be logical for the firm which wants to maximize its net worth.[4] This may be seen by means of an example.

A firm wishes to choose one of two investment opportunities, each of which requires an initial investment of $10,000. Opportunity *A* will produce a cash inflow of $800 at the end of the first year and $10,800 at the end of the second year. Opportunity *B* will bring in $10,000 at the end of the first year and $1,100 at the end of the second. The present worth of

---

[4]For an explanation of the task of establishing objectives, see Harold L. Timms, *Introduction to Operations Management* (Irwin Series in Operations Management [Homewood, Ill.: Richard D. Irwin, Inc., 1967]), chap. 3.

opportunity *A* will be zero for an interest rate of 8 percent, and thus this is *A*'s rate of return. For *B* the rate of return is 10 percent. If the firm chose so as to maximize the rate of return, it would prefer *B*. Suppose, however, that the firm can invest its money at 5 percent ordinarily. Using 5 percent interest the present worth for *A* is $558 and for *B* is $522. Since two years is involved in each case, the future worths at the end of that time would also be greater for opportunity *A* than for *B*. In other words, if the firm can invest the cash flows from these projects at 5 percent, it would have more money and greater net worth at the end of two years if it selected *A*. If this was the firm's objective, and it is a common one, it would have been illogical to have been guided by a principle of maximizing the rate of return.

Leasing

Many major pieces of equipment, such as automatic data processing systems, may be either leased or purchased on an instalment buying plan. Either of these methods may have the important result of conserving the supply of capital which the firm has available. Naturally, one would expect to pay something for this advantage. In spite of the fact that leasing may be more costly than buying, firms in industries such as petroleum refining, aircraft, chemicals, drugs, and retail food merchandising are currently engaged in leasing their equipment. Industrial property may be sold and then leased back again. Transportation equipment including trucks, automobiles, and railroad cars may be rented.

The basic idea is to avoid tying up capital in equipment if it can be used more profitably in other ways. Instead of laying out the capital when the asset is acquired, the firm makes its payments as the asset is used. This, however, may be expensive. As an example, consider a piece of equipment which could be purchased for $100,000. To rent this equipment the payments required might be something like those suggested in the three contracts in the following table.

Year	Contract 1	Contract 2	Contract 3
1	$38,000	$32,000	$26,000
2	24,000	25,000	24,000
3	13,000	18,000	24,000
4	10,000	10,000	11,000
5	10,000	10,000	10,000
6	10,000	10,000	10,000
7	10,000	10,000	10,000

These contracts differ also in the time at which the firm might be permitted to terminate the contract. Contract 1 might permit termination after one year, contract 2, after two years, and contract 3, at any time after three years. Clearly, in the decision to enter into such a contract, the firm must be interested not only in the reduction in capital requirements but also in the cost of renting the equipment, which depends crucially on how long the equipment will be required. In the following table the present worths of the rental payments are compared for various service lives.

Life	Contract 1	Contract 2	Contract 3
1.	$ 38,000	. . .	. . .
2.	60,430	$ 55,365	. . .
3.	71,784	71,086	$69,392
4.	79,947	79,249	78,371
5.	87,576	86,878	86,000
6.	94,706	94,008	93,130
7.	101,369	100,671	99,793

We have assumed an interest rate of 7 percent and payment of rentals at the beginning of each year. Whether or not rental turns out to be less costly than outright purchase depends on the pattern of salvage values and on the anticipated life over which the equipment will be used.

Tax Considerations

The firm is subject to a variety of taxes, some of which serve to complicate the evaluation of investment projects. Full-time tax specialists are usually required to develop a suitable tax strategy, but some basic considerations might serve to indicate how these specialists can be helpful. For example, the federal corporate income tax requires payments based on "taxable income" each year. Taxable income is defined by the tax laws in great detail, indicating what revenues must be included and what expenses may be deducted. It is these deductions which receive much attention, both in formulating the tax strategy of the firm and in the analysis of investment decisions.

Depreciation

Under the tax law, permanent tangible property with a useful life of more than one year may be depreciated in computing taxable income. Machinery, equipment, trucks, and so on are typical examples. Some types of intangible property, such as patents and copyrights, may also be depreciated. Land and inventories may not be depreciated for tax purposes.

In computing depreciation deductions the firm must establish a useful life and salvage value for the asset in question, and then select a method of depreciation. For tax purposes, as we shall show presently, it is to the advantage of the firm to select the shortest possible useful life. The life selected, however, must be acceptable to the Internal Revenue Service. There is a possibility that the service life allowed for tax purposes may differ from the actual service life of the asset as employed by the firm. Since the amount of depreciation which may be deducted obviously depends on the salvage value as well, the Internal Revenue Service also keeps a careful watch on it.

The tax law allows the firm to use any reasonable method of depreciation which is consistently employed. The ordinary methods are straight line, fixed percentage of a declining balance, and the sum of the years' digits method. The fixed percentage of a declining balance method is limited to percentages no greater than twice the straight line rate. Thus, for an asset having a useful life of ten years, the straight line method would lead to an annual depreciation equal to 10 percent of the difference between investment and salvage value. The fixed percentage method in this case would be limited to 20 percent.

Depreciation in year j using the fixed percentage of a declining balance method is given by

$$d(j) = pI(1 - p)^{j-1}$$

Depreciation at the straight line rate would charge a fraction $1/n$ each year, thus the tax laws permit a fixed percentage $p = 2/n$. The depreciation in year j using this percentage will be

$$d(j) = \frac{2}{n} I\left(1 - \frac{2}{n}\right)^{j-1}$$

This is equivalent to assuming a salvage value of

$$I\left(1 - \frac{2}{n}\right)^{n}$$

Since this plan may not result in full depreciation over the service life of the asset, the Internal Revenue Service permits the firm to switch to straight line depreciation at any time during the service life. Thus the firm may find itself with an asset which has been depreciated using a fixed percentage method with $p = 2/n$ for years $1, 2, \ldots, j - 1$. The undepreciated value of the asset at the beginning of year j (the end of year $j - 1$) will be

$$I\left(1 - \frac{2}{n}\right)^{j-1}$$

The firm may switch to a straight line method in which the depreciation for the years j, $(j = 1, \ldots, n)$ would be

$$d(j) = \frac{I\left(1 - \frac{2}{n}\right)^{j-1} - S}{n - j + 1} \qquad \text{for } j = 1, \ldots, n$$

The firm will find it advantageous to switch to this method in the first year for which the depreciation thus calculated by the straight line expression is greater than or equal to that calculated by the fixed percentage of the declining balance method.

The problem of selecting a method of depreciation for tax purposes is often approached on the basis of the following principle. If the firm uses a nonzero interest rate to discount future receipts and disbursements, then any method which will postpone the payment of taxes will be advantageous, in that it will reduce the present worth of the tax payments. This principle does not suggest the possibility of reducing total taxes over a period of time, but simply of postponing the tax outlays and thus reducing their present worth. In decisions where a present worth principle of choice is employed, this principle is of real importance.

Consider a depreciable asset which requires an initial investment of $11,000 and will have a useful life of five years and a salvage value of $1,000 at that time. The asset will earn an annual income, before taxes and depreciation, of $5,000. We will show, first, that no matter what method of depreciation is used, the total tax payments over the life of the asset will remain constant. Assume a tax rate of 50 percent.

Straight Line Depreciation

Year	Depreciation	Taxable Income	Tax
1	$2,000	$3,000	$1,500
2	2,000	3,000	1,500
3	2,000	3,000	1,500
4	2,000	3,000	1,500
5	2,000	3,000	1,500

Total Tax Outlay........$7,500

Fixed Percentage of a Declining Balance (40 percent)

Year	Depreciation	Taxable Income	Tax
1	$4,400	$ 600	$ 300
2	2,640	2,360	1,180
3	1,584	3,416	1,708
4	950	4,050	2,025
5	420*	4,574	2,287

Total Tax Outlay........$7,500

*Only $426 depreciation in the fifth year since the total depreciation must not exceed $10,000.

Sum of Years' Digits

Year	Depreciation	Taxable Income	Tax
1	$3,333	$1,667	$ 833
2	2,667	2,333	1,166
3	2,000	3,000	1,500
4	1,333	3,667	1,835
5	667	4,333	2,167

Total Tax Outlay........$7,500

Now suppose the firm uses an interest rate of 10 percent and bases decisions on present worths. The present worth of the tax outlays in each of the above cases is

Method	Present Worth of Tax Outlays
Straight line	$5,686
Fixed percentage of declining balance	5,225
Sum of years' digits	5,443

Thus, from the point of view of present worth, the firm would elect in this case the fixed percentage of a declining balance method. We have used the maximum allowable percentage of 40 percent in this example. Clearly, the pattern of depreciation can have a significant influence on the present worth of tax outays over the life of the asset and thus an influence over the present worth of income after taxes. Thus, the pattern of depreciation may be relevant in choices where taxes are to be considered.

Unfortunately there is no one best method of depreciation for tax purposes. The table below shows that the choice between the fixed percentage method (with $p = 2/n$ and switch to straight line where advantageous) and the sum of the years' digits method may depend both upon interest rate and upon service life. The table shows the present worth of depreciation charges for an asset costing $10,000 and having no salvage value. To minimize the present worth of tax payments, one would seek to maximize the present worth of depreciation charges.

Interest Rate	Service Life (Years)	Present Worth of Depreciation Charges SYD	FPDB*
.10	5	$8,061	$8,110
.10	10	7,010	6,853
.01	6	9,739	9,736
.10	6	7,832	7,825
.20	6	6,368	6,382
.30	6	5,329	5,370

*Assumes switch to straight line depreciation where advantageous.

It should be noted, also, that in decisions among alternative projects, the mix of depreciable and nondepreciable assets for each of the projects may have a bearing upon choice. Suppose, for instance, we consider the above machine having an investment of $11,000 and a salvage value of $1,000 after a five-year service life as one alternative. This is to be compared with a second alternative which involves the purchase of a plot of land in the center of a city to be operated as a parking lot. The land cannot be depreciated under the tax laws. Suppose the land is purchased for $11,000, is to be used for five years, and then sold. It is expected that its selling price at that time will be $11,000. Assume the net profit before taxes for the parking lot is expected to be $3,600 each year. This will also be the taxable income. We suppose further that the parking lot income will be subject to a project tax rate of 50 percent, as with the machine.

For the parking lot the taxable income of $3,600 each year will result in a tax of $1,800 and an income after taxes of $1,800. If we neglect interest, this means the total income after taxes over the five-year period will be $5(1,800) = $9,000. Since the land does not decline in price we need not be concerned with recovering the investment out of income. To simplify the computations, let us consider the machine under a policy of straight line depreciation. Again neglecting interest, the investment in the machine will yield an income after taxes and depreciation (investment recovery) of $7,500 over the five years. On this basis the parking lot seems advantageous.

However, consider the present worths of the two projects using an interest rate of 10 percent. The actual receipts and disbursements for the machine, using straight line depreciation, are:

Year	Receipts		Disbursements
	Depreciation	*Income after Taxes*	
0...............	...	.....	$11,000
1...............	$2,000	$1,500	
2...............	2,000	1,500	
3...............	2,000	1,500	
4...............	2,000	1,500	
5...............	2,000	1,500 (plus $1,000 salvage)	

The present worth of this series of receipts and disbursements is

$$\{\$2,000 + \$1,500\}(3.791) + 1,000(.6209) - 11,000 = \$2,889.40$$

For the parking lot the actual cash receipts and disbursements are:

Year	Receipts (*Income after Taxes*)	Disbursements
0....................	$1,800	$11,000
1....................	1,800	
2....................	1,800	
3....................	1,800	
4....................	1,800	
5....................	1,800 (plus $11,000 resale price for land)	

The present worth here is

$$1,800(3.791) + 11,000(.6209) - 11,000 = \$2,653.70$$

The parking lot, on the basis of a present worth criterion, woud not be selected in preference to the investment in the machine. The point here is simply that, when taxes are considered and when a present worth principle of choice is used, the proportion of depreciable and nondepreciable assets composing each alternative may influence choice.

Borrowed Funds

Interest paid on indebtedness is deductible as a business expense under the present laws. This means that a project which is financed with borrowed capital may have its taxable income reduced by the amount of the interest involved. The reader should carefully distinguish interest used in the analysis of decisions which does not actually represent the cost of borrowed money, from interest which is actually paid for borrowed funds.

The former is not deductible for tax purposes, while the latter is.

Consider, for example, the machine discussed previously. Suppose the machine is financed by means of a loan of $11,000 which is to be repaid at the rate of $2,000 each year for the first four years and $3,000 at the end of the fifth year. Interest is paid at the rate of 10 percent on the unpaid balance of the loan.

Year	Gross Income	Repayment	Unpaid Balance	Interest	Income before Taxes	Tax
1........	$5,000	$2,000	$11,000	$1,100	$1,900	$ 950
2........	5,000	2,000	9,000	900	2,100	1,050
3........	5,000	2,000	7,000	700	2,300	1,150
4........	5,000	2,000	5,000	500	2,500	1,250
5........	5,000	3,000	3,000	300	2,700	1,350

Now if we examine the total income over the five years, it will clearly be less using borrowed funds than it would have been if we had used funds that had been considered essentially costless. The point is that, in each year, the deductibility of interest has generated a tax saving. Thus, in the first year, if the machine is financed out of equity capital, the tax will be $1,500, assuming straight line depreciation. Using borrowed funds the tax is only $950, a saving of $550. This means that the cost of borrowed funds was actually

$$\$1,100 - \$550 = \$550$$

thus cutting the interest rate in half. This ratio carries through for the succeeding years, leaving the firm with an actual interest rate on the loan of only 5 percent. While the firm might be unwilling to borrow funds at 10 percent, it might choose to do so in view of the tax savings which reduces the interest rate to 5 percent.

Research and Development

Expenses for research and development are also deductible for tax computations. By reasoning similar to that used in connection with borrowed funds, it can be shown that any research done by the firm whose effective tax rate is 50 percent actually costs the firm only 50 cents for each dollar spent. This applies also to research done for the firm by other organizations. This means that research can be a tremendous bargain for the firm, and the government effectively encourages it. This is the basis for the remark, "Research dollars are only 50-cent dollars."

A variety of other tax provisions may be relevant to any given decision—for example, the provisions for taxing short- and long-term capital gains or losses, the treatment of repairs, replacements, and improvements, and so on. Our point, however, is simply to suggest their possible relevance for decision making and to encourage the analyst to consult the tax specialist.

PROBLEMS

1. A firm brings out a small computer which it hopes to sell to small businesses. The computer sells for $10,000, but potential customers will need financing assistance in order to buy it. Several financing plans are being considered:

   a) A $4,000 down payment followed by 20 annual payments. If interest is charged at 6 percent, what should be the amount of the annual payments?

   b) Payments of $872 each year for 20 years after an initial down payment. What should be the amount of the down payment if 6 percent interest is to be charged?

   c) A down payment of $3,000, ten equal annual payments, and a final payment of $3,000 at the end of ten years. What should be the amount of the annual payments if 6 percent interest is charged?

2. A firm faces a choice among the three machines described below:

	Machine A	Machine B	Machine C
Initial cost	$40,000	$42,000	$49,000
Service life	8 years for all machines		
Annual operating costs	12,000	10,500	9,000
Salvage value	4,000	4,000	5,000

   a) If the firm requires a return of 10 percent of its investments, which machine would be preferred?

   b) Which machine would be preferred if the service lives were 8 years for machine *A*, 10 years for machine *B*, and 12 years for machine *C*?

   c) Repeat part (*a*) for interest rates of 0, 5, and 15 percent.

3. A project requiring an investment of $16,000 is expected to have an earning life of 8 years and no salvage value. The estimated annual income from the project is $10,000 with annual operating expenses of $7,000, not including taxes.

   a) Find the rate of return on the project before taxes.

   b) Find the rate of return after taxes, if the effective tax rate is 50 percent. The project is to be depreciated by the straight-line method over 8 years.

SUGGESTIONS FOR FURTHER STUDY

BIERMAN, HAROLD, JR., and SMIDT, SEYMOUR. *The Capital Budgeting Decision.* New York: The Macmillan Co., 1960.

DAVIDSON, SIDNEY, and DRAKE, DAVID F. "Capital Budgeting and the Best Tax Depreciation Method," *Journal of Business,* Vol. 34, No. 4. (October, 1961).

GRANT, EUGENE L., and IRESON, W. GRANT. *Principles of Engineering Economy.* 4th ed. New York: The Ronald Press Co., 1960.

MORRIS, WILLIAM T. *The Analysis of Management Decisions.* Homewood, Ill.: Richard D. Irwin, Inc., 1964.

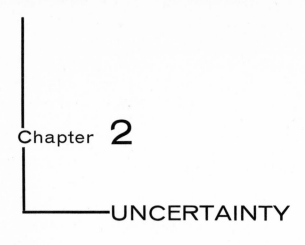

Chapter 2

UNCERTAINTY

Management Responses to Uncertainty

AT ANY STAGE in the evaluation of an investment proposal management's attitude toward the predicted cash flows reflects their evaluation of the uncertainty surrounding these future events. The critical question is whether evaluation has sufficiently reduced the uncertainty so that management may now make a decision, or whether further efforts to reduce uncertainty are needed. Thus at any stage in the proposal's development management may feel prepared to make its decision or more effort may be devoted to collecting data and making judgments. In the latter case we will suppose that the objective of the firm's management information system is to make the uncertainties explicit, perhaps by expressing them in terms of probabilities. If the uncertainties can be made explicit then several advantages follow:

1. Uncertainties can be communicated, checked, and refined throughout the capital budgeting system. Without explicit expression, they tend to be suppressed and one finds highly uncertain estimates produced at the operating levels being accepted as certain statements of the future at higher levels in the firm. It is important to have a method of transmitting uncertainty.

2. The logic of probability theory can be used to help management make consistent decisions in highly complex situations. That is, from explicit expressions of uncertainty about simple events well within one's experience, probability theory can be used to obtain logically consistent expressions of uncertainty in complex events which are beyond one's immediate experience.

3. If uncertainties can be made explicit, rather than remain exclusively a matter of implicit managerial judgment, then management will be far more willing and able to delegate important aspects of the capital

24

budgeting process. Delegation, as will be discussed in Chapter 6, is a central consideration in the design of effective capital budgeting systems.

Thus it is supposed that the aim of the firm's management information system is to collect data or obtain judgments from experts or experienced managers which will lead to an explicit evaluation of the uncertainty in an investment decision. By this means, future events are to be predicted in terms of probability distributions and the resulting decisions will be what have been traditionally called decisions in the face of risk.

The Management Information System

Hopefully the firm's information system will provide data, both from its own experience and from outside the firm, which will permit the prediction of cash flows in terms of probability distributions. This may prove to be a difficult and expensive undertaking.

Suppose a firm is considering the purchase of one of several alternative production machines and that experience and preliminary investigation reveal that the following information is needed for each alternative:

Price	Output
Installation cost	Scrap rate
Operating costs	Service life
Maintenance cost	Salvage value

Assuming this decision is important enough to warrant a rather detailed analysis, we will suggest some of the sources from which basic information might typically be obtained, and in the next chapter illustrate some of the techniques which might be used to process this information for inclusion in the analysis.

The price of each machine would most likely be obtained through a direct quotation from the manufacturer. The installation cost might be the result of a detailed estimate by the plant millwright based upon data obtained from similar jobs done in the past. If the installation is to be performed by the manufacturer or by an outside contractor, quotations might be obtained from these sources. If the major difference in operating costs among the alternatives will arise out of differing direct labor requirements, the firm's time study department might be consulted. Either from performance times observed on similar machines doing similar operations, or from a system of synthetic time values, an estimate of the direct labor requirements might be obtained. From the personnel department or the accounting department an estimate of the wage rates from the skill levels involved could be obtained, which would yield a direct labor cost estimate when combined with the performance time estimates. Maintenance costs might be separated into costs associated with regularly scheduled maintenance activity or preventive maintenance, those costs which result from breakdowns, and repairs which require unscheduled maintenance effort. Once a preventive maintenance program is established, the times, skills, wage rates, and thus the costs may be estimated by recourse to the information available from the time study department, the accounting department, and the records of the maintenance department itself. The frequency and severity of breakdowns are much more difficult to estimate, and are typically obtained either from records of the firm's experience with similar machines or from data furnished by the manufacturer describing the failure patterns of his equipment under operating conditions similar to those which exist within the firm.

The estimated output of each alternative is usually based upon the manufacturer's specifications of feeds, speeds, power, and capacity for his equipment, in combination with estimates from the time study department of human performance times wherever they are involved. The scrap rate of each machine may be difficult to estimate, but some basis may be obtained from the manufacturer's claims as to precision and accuracy and from the records of the quality control department for similar machine and job situations. The service life depends heavily on the firm's policy with respect to machine replacement. How does the firm decide when to replace a machine and when to continue its use? The problems of formulating replacement policy are examined in detail in Chapter 4. Once this policy is clearly established, data from the firm's own records or from those of the manufacturer may provide a basis for estimating service life from the study of similar machines. Salvage value is usually a function of the age of the machine, as well as its condition and degree of obsolescence. Often the best one can do is to obtain data on current and past market prices for used machinery as a basis for estimating the salvage values of the alternatives under consideration.

Given this sort of data, the techniques of inferential statistics may be brought to bear. The basic tactic is to formulate probabilistic or random models for the cash flows and then test to see if the models are reasonably consistent with the data. For example, given a sample of salvage values for five-year-old machines of a certain type, one might raise the hypothesis that this salvage value could be viewed reasonably as a normally distributed random variable with some specified mean and variance. Statistical techniques then may be used to test the reasonableness of this model in the light of the data. In this way, one comes to view future cash flows as random variables.

In many cases, it is difficult, very expensive, or even impossible to obtain the relevant data. Investment decisions often involve contingencies, or future events which cannot readily be forecast by means of available data. Events such as research discoveries, technological innovations, the emergence of new competitors and so on may not yield readily to predictions based on past data. In these cases expert judgment and management experience must be sought, but again it will be supposed that the uncertainty associated with these judgments is to be expressed in probabilistic terms. These expressions are generally spoken of as subjective or personalistic probabilities.

Subjective Probability

Just how such expressions of uncertainty in the language of probability theory are to be obtained and how they can be logically manipulated are matters of some subtlety. The use of random models as ways of expressing a manager's uncertainty about future events is today a hypothesis whose effectiveness must be tested in practice, rather than an established feature of many management decision systems. Yet it is a hypothesis which promises some very considerable benefits and thus seems worth investigating to many systems designers. The basic issues are roughly outlined below.

Suppose we assume that a manager chooses in risky situations so as to maximize his expected or average profit, an assumption we will shortly consider in detail. Suppose further we described to this manager a lottery in which there were 100 tickets to be sold and the prize is K dollars or something which has for him a utility equivalent to that of K dollars. We offer him any one of the tickets and, if the decision maker was indifferent as to which ticket he held, we could then say that the drawing of any ticket was an event with which he associated the subjective probability .01. This lottery may be used as a measuring device in the following manner. To find the subjective probability he associates with the event "he will win a certain contract" we ask him, "How many tickets in the lottery would you find equivalent to the prospect of winning a prize of utility K in the event that you win the contract?" If he is able to answer this question, after due consideration, by saying that he would be indifferent between 20 tickets in the lottery and the prospect of winning the prize if he is awarded the contract, then we would call .20 his subjective probability of the event "he wins the contract." If we wished we could start with a lottery of 1,000 tickets and perhaps learn that his subjective probability is .203.

It would be convenient to be able to use the theorems of probability theory to make calculations of the subjective probabilities of complex events based on the subjective probabilities of simple events. The theorems are used in this way in the case of relative frequencies. To make this reasonable, we assign subjective probability zero to any event which the decision maker believes is impossible and subjective probability one to any event which he feels is certain to occur. Further, we insist that the sum of the subjective probabilities of a mutually exclusive and collectively exhaustive set of events must be one. For any two mutually exclusive events, we insist that the subjective probability of either one or the other be equal to the sum of their individual subjective probabilities. If the results obtained from a decision maker are not in agreement with these axioms, then we must ask him to reconsider and correct his "inconsistency." If his subjective probabilities do agree with them, then we have some justification for using them to predict consistent choices according to the theorems of probability theory. Recommendations based on subjective probabilities would be predictions of consistent choices for the decision maker.

Several important points should be noted about the notion of subjective probability.

1. The decision maker must be able to think about his attitudes toward risk and answer the sort of questions which have been suggested. Without doubt this is a difficult sort of thing to bring off in actuality. Inconsistencies may arise, the results may be unreliable, and the whole thing may appear quite "fuzzy" to the manager.

2. Reasonable men could be expected to have similar subjective probabilities for events with which they have had similar experience. Thus subjective probabilities should not be matters of widely divergent attitudes, when some experience is available.

3. In many routine situations, a manager's subjective probabilities will be determined by routine data collection and analysis methods. In these cases, the determination of probabilities can be delegated to the analyst and the manager may be freed for the more difficult decisions.

4. Relative frequencies (sometimes called objective probabilities) are themselves the product of considerable subjective judgment by the analyst. They differ mainly in that the data on which they are based and the rules for processing the data are made more explicit.

5. If a manager's experience is not considered most extensive and most relevant on a particular question, then an expert may be brought in. The expert is someone believed to have considerable knowledge and experience on the matter in question. He is then integrated into the decision process by obtaining from him his subjective probabilities. One could suggest certain qualifications that might be used as tests to determine a person's admissibility as an expert. For example, we might require that he

   a) have personalistic probabilities which are reasonably stable over time, providing he receives no new evidence,

   b) have probabilities which are affected in the right direction by new evidence,

   c) be selected for his past predictive performance, his demonstrated record of success and accuracy.

Thus a good deal of what is most subjective about subjective probabilities would be removed in the case of the expert. He is in fact treated as a kind of powerful computer in the decision process. He digests rich and complex past experience, producing the probabilities as his output.

Thus we suppose that either by explicit methods of data collection and statistical analysis or by means of subjective probability, or by some combination of the two, the uncertainties surrounding future cash flow can be expressed in probabilistic terms. Before considering the resulting investment decisions, we turn briefly to a most important aspect of the design of management decision systems.

Adaptive Information Systems

Every firm may be thought of as a leaning or adaptive organism, and a critical task of the systems designer is to make this process of benefiting from past experience as effective as possible. Systems which permit the firm to make explicit its process of adaptation are now under active development. We offer only an extremely simple example to illustrate the importance of this aspect of systems design.

Perhaps one of the most obvious, and yet widely neglected, opportunities for organizational learning arises out of the simple possibility of comparing past forecasts with actual events. This can be done whether forecasts are produced by explicit prediction techniques, implicit judgment processes, or the usual combination of both, by recording them and comparing them with the actual outcomes. This is done by the firm which follows up its capital investment decisions with a "postaudit," designed to see if their investments are performing in accordance with the forecasts on which the decisions were based. It is done by the company president who keeps track of his sales manager's forecasts and then compares them with actual sales data. This is especially useful when forecasts are made repeatedly and the actual events are observable within a reasonable period of time. Consider, for example, the jobbing foundry which forecasts the cost of producing various castings for its customers and then measures the actual costs of production. There are many instances in which firms forecast costs and then are able to observe the actual costs which result. In these situations it may be valuable to keep track of the effectiveness of the forecasts made as a basis for improving the process.

Let us suppose that it is possible in such a situation to obtain data on forecasted and actual costs for various jobs. Let

$$E_i = \text{forecast of the cost for job } i$$
$$A_i = \text{actual cost for job } i$$
$$e_i = \frac{E_i}{A_i} = \text{error ratio for job } i$$

Instead of using the ratio of forecast to actual cost as a measure of error, we might have used some other function such as

$$\frac{E_i - A_i}{A_i}$$

We will, however, proceed using e_i as previously defined. One might expect that, if e_i were obtained for a number of jobs and tabulated, it might be reasonably described by a probability distribution $f(e)$. Some statistical analysis would be necessary to support this supposition, since e_i might differ markedly among jobs of different sizes, types, or degrees of complexity. However, if we are able to obtain an $f(e)$ for the class of jobs under consideration, then it is useful to compute the mean and variance of the error ratio.

$$\bar{e} = \sum ef(e)$$

$$\sigma_e^2 = \sum (e - \bar{e})^2 f(e)$$

The mean of the error ratio, $\bar{e}$, provides a measure of the accuracy, bias, or validity of the forecasts. If the mean is equal to one, then we may say that our forecasts are accurate in the sense that on the average they are equal to the actual cost we are attempting to estimate. If the mean of the error ratio differs from one, the amount of this difference is a measure of the bias in our forecasting process. If, for example, $\bar{e} = 1.05$, then we may say that on the average our predictions are 5 percent too high. If this is the case then it would be sensible to correct our forecasts in the future to adjust for this bias. We might then work with a corrected forecast, E'_i, computed from the relation

$$E'_i = \frac{E_i}{\bar{e}}$$

The alternative to this method might be to investigate the process in an attempt to trace back the source of this bias and correct it where it originates. This can only be done if the prediction process is explicit.

The variance of the error ratio is a measure of the precision of process. It reflects the pattern of dispersion of our forecasts in terms of the average of their squared deviations from their mean. This is also referred to as the reliability of the process.

There is no simple short-run way to overcome lack of precision. It may be taken directly into account in decision making as will be done with decisions under risk. It may also be possible to review the process, looking for the steps in this process which are the major contributors to the variance of our predictions, and seek to reduce this variance at its source. Time, experience, and the accumulation of larger samples of data should have the effect of improving the precision of our predictions.

In this example, of course, the predictions or judgments are producing only single-valued forecasts. No expression of the uncertainty surrounding these forecasts is assumed. If the uncertainty were to be expressed in probabilistic terms as has been suggested previously, then the learning process would be somewhat richer and more complex. In such cases Bayesian Decision Theory provides a possible logic for the systems designer.

We return now to consideration of investment decisions in which the uncertainties have been made explicit in the language of probability theory. Decisions involving the analysis of probabilities and cash flows may be referred to as decisions under conditions of risk.

Management Decisions under Risk

If the analyst could get data on the manager's preferences, then perhaps a model could be developed which would "explain" or agree with the observations and serve as a basis for predicting his preferences among outcomes beyond those observed. The analyst could then use the model as a basis for making recommendations which he predicts are consistent with the manager's values. If the analyst and the manager agree as to the alternatives, futures, and outcomes involved in the decision, and if the analyst's model of the manager's preferences is successful, then presumably the recommendation will be accepted. In this sense the recommendation would be consistent with the manager's own attitudes. He would want to accept the result because it is the same conclusion he himself would have reached had he taken the time to do the analysis which has been done for him. The management might then be willing to delegate (perhaps with only perfunctory approval) those routine decisions for which the alternatives and outcomes can be determined by routine methods and for which the analyst's model of his preferences is applicable. This relieves the manager to devote more of his time to those difficult decisions which really require his experience and judgment. The manager may further become willing to accept the assistance of the analyst in finding consistent preferences among complex outcomes which are perhaps beyond his immediate experience. The analyst, beginning with the simple expressions of preferences reflecting the manager's experience, reasons with the aid of the model to reach deductively consistent preference statements for complex outcomes. The manager may find that this relieves him of many hours of difficult study in complicated decision problems.

The study of management responses to risk may be approached with a program similar in principle to this. Now, however, it will be useful to study a manager's attitudes toward actions which involve probabilistic combinations of outcomes rather than sure outcomes as before. As will become evident, it is difficult to divorce a manager's attitude toward profit from his attitude toward the chances of making various amounts of profit. By studying his preferences in risky situations we will try to capture in a model his attitudes toward risk, profit, and loss. As before, we will try to make some observations which will serve as a basis for such a model of how he responds in the face of risk. Assuming the manager wishes to be consistent in the sense of not contradicting himself, he would be interested in accepting recommendations based on such a model. For the analyst, the model becomes a principle of choice which he uses to process the data describing a decision under risk into a recommendation for management action.

Developing a Model of Attitudes toward Risk

Let us begin with some data indicating the responses of a particular manager to some risky alternatives. Suppose we confront this manager with two contracts (or gambles, or business opportunities) which are very simply described so as to make it reasonably easy for him to state his preferences. Contract A requires an investment of $100,000 the results of which depend on three possible future events. Possible future S_1 will bring the manager a profit of $200,000 if he accepts contract A, while possible futures S_2 and S_3 result in a complete loss of the original $100,000. Contract B requires an investment of $40,000 which will be lost in the event of S_2 but which will yield a profit of $70,000 in the case of either S_1 or S_2. The manger's decision is whether to accept contract A or contract B (but not both), or to accept neither. For convenience we will label the action "accept neither contract" with the name, contract C. We will suppose that the analyst and the manager agree that the probabilities (whatever their basis) are

$$p_1 = .50 \qquad p_2 = .10 \qquad p_3 = .40$$

The decision is summarized in the matrix below:

	$p = .50$ S_1	$p_2 = .10$ S_2	$p_3 = .40$ S_3
Contract A	$200,000	$- $100,000	$- $100,000
Contract B	$ 70,000	$ 70,000	$- $ 40,000
Contract C	0	0	0

Now we will suppose that the manager confronted with these three mutually exclusive actions, is able after due consideration to express his preferences. Suppose, for example, he reports that he would most prefer contract B and would choose contract C (accept neither) in preference to contract A. Thus he ranks these actions

1. Contract B
2. Contract C
3. Contract A

Considering this statement as our empirical evidence, can we develop a model or principle of choice which will agree with it or "explain" it? Conventionally in decisions under risk it is suggested that we compute the average or expected profit associated with each action, and choose so as to maximize this quantity. Does this principle provide a model consistent with the results of our experiment?
Let

$$E(a_i) \; = \; \text{expected profit for alternative } i \; (\text{dollars})$$

For contract A

$$E(A) \; = \; (.50)(\$200{,}000) \; + \; (.10)(-\$100{,}000) \; + \; (.40)(-\$100{,}000)$$
$$= \$50{,}000$$

For contract B

$$E(B) \; = \; (.50)(\$70{,}000) \; + \; (.10)(\$70{,}000) \; + \; (.40)(-\$40{,}000)$$
$$= \$26{,}000$$

For contract C

$$E(C) \; = \; 0$$

Summarizing these results and comparing them with the manager's reported preferences we have

Action	Expected Profit	Manager's Ranking
Contract A	$50,000	3
Contract B	26,000	1
Contract C	0	2

Clearly maximizing expected profit fails as a model of this manager's preferences in this experiment. Seeking further clues, perhaps we discuss the matter with him. Possibly he suggests something like this: "I would rather do nothing than accept contract A because, with the limited working capital we now have, the loss of $100,000 would put the firm in very serious trouble. A 50 percent chance of making $200,000 is not good enough to offset the 50 percent chance that we will lose the $100,000. On the other hand, contract B is acceptable because we could weather the loss of $40,000 well enough, and the chances of a profit are better." This manager seems averse to risk in a rather reasonable way. To understand his behavior, we will have to consider the actions available to him not simply in terms of expected profit, but in terms of the possible profits and losses, together with the probabilities of each. However, the expected profit principle would have been satisfactory if the choice had involved only contracts B and C. We will return to this point later.

Suppose we had been able to arrange three new contracts labeled A', B', and C' whose conditions were

A': a loss of $200,000 with probability .35
      a profit of $400,000 with probability .65
B': a loss of $200,000 with probability .28
      a profit of $400,000 with probability .72
C': a loss of $200,000 with probability .30
      a profit of $400,000 with probability .70

If we had asked him to rank these three mutually exclusive actions, the decision would have been both easy for him to make and easy for us to explain. The dollar amounts of profit and loss are the same for each contract, and surely a reasonable man would choose the contract which maximizes the probability of a $400,000 profit and minimizes the probability of a $200,000 loss. Thus we would expect the contracts to be ranked

Contract	Manager's Rank
A'	3
B'	1
C'	2

Now we will show a rather remarkable thing. The original decision among contracts A, B, and C can be reduced to the easy one among contracts A', B', and C' in a way which makes them equivalent in the opinion of a logically consistent manager. Such a manager would find himself indifferent between contract A and contract A' and thus consider the two equivalent. He would hold similar opinions about B and B' as well as C and C'. Thus if he were consistent he would prefer contract B' in the easy, reduced decision and contract B in the original decision. This scheme for reducing decisions to equivalent ones, in which the manager would choose so as to maximize the probability of a given amount of profit (or the probability of "success"), provides the basis for our model of his preferences.

To do this, we approach risky decisions from a somewhat different viewpoint. Suppose we may eventually be interested in the manager's attitudes toward contracts involving losses as great as $200,000 and profits up to $400,000. We take these two extreme amounts and form a basic contract or "reference" contract which we will use as a sort of measuring device. The basic contract is one which promises a profit of $400,000 with probability p, and a loss of $200,000 with probability $1 - p$.

We then approach the manager with the following question, "If you had already incurred a debt of $100,000, and someone offered to take over your obligation if you would enter into a contract which promised $400,000 with probability p and $200,000 loss with probability $1 - p$, what would the value of p have to be before you would just be willing to do this?" We suppose that after considerable reflection the manager is able to say that he would be indifferent if p were .40. We will interpret this result by saying, "He is indifferent between a sure loss of $100,000 and our basic contract with p, the probability of making $400,000, equal to .40." Let us call p the probability of success in the basic contract, for short.

Next, we ask him to suppose that he is offered the basic contract and he must choose between it and doing nothing. We wish to learn what the probability of success in the basic contract would have to be, before he would just be willing to accept it. We will suppose that he is able to say that if p were .70 he would just be indifferent between the basic contract and doing nothing. We repeat precisely the same sort of question for a loss of $40,000 and profits of $70,000 and $200,000. In each case we ask him to compare the amount in question for sure, against the reference or basic contract, and to report the value of p for which he would be indifferent. Let us imagine the results are those summarized below.

Outcome	Value of p in Equiv- alent Basic Contract
− $100,000	.40
− 40,000	.60
0	.70
70,000	.80
200,000	.90

Using this scheme it would be reasonable to expect indifference between a loss of $200,000 and the basic gamble with $p = 0$. Similarly, we would expect indifference between the basic contract with probability of success 1 and a sure $400,000 profit.

Consider now the matrix in which we summarized the original decision together with the preference statements we have subsequently obtained. The manager has indicated that he is indifferent between our basic contract with probability of success .90 and a sure profit of $200,000. We now suppose that if we alter the original decision by removing the $200,000 and replacing it with our basic contract having a probability of success of .90, we do not alter the value of alternative A in the opinion of the manager. That is, we assume that if the $200,000 profit in contract A is replaced by the basic contract with $p = .90$, then the manager's attitude toward alternative A remains unchanged. If, after all, he is indifferent in the way in which he has reported, then we should be able to make this change without altering his view of alternative A. Using this important assumption, we continue substituting for the outcomes in the original matrix, the various basic contracts for which he has indicated indifference. The transformed matrix now contains the alternatives A', B', and C'. It appears below.

	$p_1 = .50$ S_1	$p_2 = .10$ S_2	$p_3 = .40$ S_3
A'	Basic contract with $p = .90$	Basic contract with $p = .40$	Basic contract with $p = .40$
B'	Basic contract with $p = .80$	Basic contract with $p = .80$	Basic contract with $p = .60$
C'	Basic contract with $p = .70$	Basic contract with $p = .70$	Basic contract with $p = .70$

We suppose, it is to be emphasized, that the values of the alternatives A', B', and C' in the transformed matrix are the same for the manager as the values of the contracts A, B, and C in the original matrix. This supposition defines in part what we mean by a reasonable and consistent manager.

Now if he chooses contract A', he will receive a profit of $400,000 with probability given by

$$(.50)(.90) + (.10)(.40) + (.40)(.40) = .65$$

and suffer a loss of $200,000 with probability:

$$(.50)(.10) + (.10)(.60) + (.40)(.60) = .35$$

This is equivalent to saying that if he chooses contract A it is quite the same as choosing the basic contract with a probability of success equal to .65. If he chooses alternative B' it is the same as choosing to receive $400,000 with probability .72 and lose $200,000 with probability .28. That is

$$(.50)(.80) + (.10)(.80) + (.40)(.60) = .72$$
$$(.50)(.20) + (.10)(.20) + (.40)(.40) = .28$$

Again this is equivalent to saying that choosing alternative B' is quite the same as choosing our basic contract with probability of success equal to .72. This, in turn, we take to be equivalent in the manager's opinion to choosing the original contract B. He has already stated that accepting neither contract A nor contract B is equivalent to accepting our basic contract with probability of success equal to .70. As before alternative C' in the transformed matrix is taken to be indifferent with respect to the original contract C (accept neither).

Now the decision represented by the transformed matrix appears quite obvious to the manager. He chooses alternative B' in preference to A' or C' since this maximizes his probability of success in the basic contract, or gives him the largest probability of making \$400,000 and thus the smallest probability of losing \$200,000. If he is consistent with his own basic expressions of preference, he will also choose contract B in the original decision. This is, in fact, what we observed.

What we have done is to reduce the original decision to an equivalent one involving only our basic alternative. Having done this, it seemed reasonable that the manager would choose so as to maximize the probability of success. If we wish to, we may assign this probability of success the name utility. The utility of any alternative is thus the probability of success in the equivalent or indifferent basic alternative.

Our results so far are summarized below.

Contract	Expected Dollar Profit	Manager's Rank	Utility
A	\$50,000	3	.65
B	26,000	1	.72
C	0	2	.70

Put another way, he already indicated that he would prefer to do nothing rather than accept our basic contract unless the probability of success is at least .70. For contract A we were able to substitute an equivalent basic contract with a probability of success of only .65. Thus, if he were consistent he would do nothing rather than accept contract A. Contract B, however, could be reduced to an equivalent basic contract with a probability of success equal to .72. This consistency would suggest that he would choose contract B in preference to no contract at all. Since maximizing the probability of success in the basic alternative seems to describe or explain his behavior rather well, we can if we wish call this probability a utility and say that the manager chooses so as to maximize his utility.

It turns out thus that the zero point on our utility scale corresponds to a loss of \$200,000, while a profit of \$400,000 has a utility of 1.00. We shall see shortly that it makes no difference where we take the zero point and what we take to be one unit of utility. We are developing an interval scale which will perform satisfactorily with an arbitrary zero point and with an arbitrary but constant unit of measurement. In this respect it is like temperature measurement with Fahrenheit or centigrade scales.

We discover then that, although a model based on maximizing expected dollar return does not seem to describe his attitudes, a model which attaches utilities to outcomes and contracts in the way we have described does indeed agree with his preferences (so far as we have observed them).

Utility

Now let us make some general statements about this method of assigning numbers, called utilities, to outcomes and contracts. Notice that we have assigned numbers or utilities to sure outcomes, say a profit of $200,000 for certain, as well as to contracts which were in fact risky alternatives, such as contract *A*. Now let us adopt the term "prospect" to stand for either of these, and use the symbol $U(P)$ to stand for the utility of a prospect *P*. Generalizing for our work so far, we could suggest that our method of assigning utilities has the property

$$U(P_1) > U(P_2)$$

if and only if the manager prefers the prospect P_1 to the prospect P_2. This is true on the basis of our observations so far, and if he acts in a consistent fashion, it will be true in general. Thus our model predicts that if he acts consistently, he will always choose the prospect which maximizes his utility.

Notice also a second property of this scheme. We have assigned the following utilities:

$$
\begin{aligned}
U(-\ \$100,000) &= .40 \\
U(\$200,000) &= .90 \\
U(\text{Contract } A) &= .65
\end{aligned}
$$

Now suppose instead of computing the expected dollar return for contract *A*, we compute the *expected utility*.

$$
\begin{aligned}
\text{Expected utility of contract } A &= (.50)U(-\ \$100,000) + (.50)U(\$200,000) \\
&= (.50)(.40) + (.50)(.90) \\
&= .65
\end{aligned}
$$

Thus, under this scheme for assigning utilities, the utility of a risky alternative is equal to its expected utility. While our expected dollar return model did not work, an expected utility model does. Thus we may reach the following important conclusion about decisions under risk: *A manager who wishes to act in a logically consistent way in any decision under risk will choose the alternative which maximizes his expected utility.*

If we could measure a manager's utilities in this way, then the problem of a principle of choice for decisions under risk would be solved. Before examining the possibilities of applying this scheme in actual management situations, let us sharpen our understanding of it.

First let us show that the zero point and the unit of measurement on the utility scale make no difference in the results. We chose $- $200,000 as the zero point and $400,000 as the unit point because it was convenient. They represented the extremes of the range in which we expected to deal. Now suppose we change the unit of measurement by multiplying all the utilities by a positive constant and change the zero point on the scale by adding a constant to all the utilities. Under this transformation the utility of a prospect $U(P)$ becomes $a + bU(P)$. Under our method of assigning utilities, the utility of a prospect is equal to its expected utility. Thus

$$U(A) = (.50)U(-\$100,000) + (.50)U(\$200,000) = .65$$
$$U(B) = (.40)U(-\$40,000) + (.60)U(\$70,000) = .72$$

For the manager whom we studied we might transform the utility scale by multiplying by a positive constant b and adding a constant a. Calling the transformed utility scale U', we have

$$U'(A) = (.50)\{a + bU(-\$100,000)\} + (.50)\{a + bU(\$200,000)\}$$
$$= a + bU(A)$$

and similarly

$$U'(B) = a + bU(B)$$

Thus any decision consistent with the original utility scale will also be consistent with the transformed utility scale.

Graphical Representation

We can get a further look at this manager's attitudes toward risk by plotting the utilities of the various amounts of money we have measured. This is done in Figure 2–1 where we have also taken the liberty of passing a smooth curve through the points. It is now clear that the value of money for this man, as we have measured it, is not proportional to the amount of money. His utility function exhibits a diminishing marginal utility for money. That is, the more money he has, the less the utility of an additional dollar.

Now consider contract A which involves a profit of $200,000 with utility .90 (point a on the utility function) and a loss of $100,000 with utility .40 (point b). Now let q be the probability with which the profit of $200,000 is received. For any q we could compute the expected dollar return from contract A:

$$q(\$200,000) + (1 - q)(-\$100,000)$$

and the expected utility for contract A:

$$q(.90) + (1 - q)(.40)$$

The utility of the contract is, as we have shown, equal to its expected utility. We now plot the points whose coordinates are the expected dollar returns and the expected utilities for values of q from zero to one. These points will fall on a straight line between a and b. The original value of q, which was .50, results in a point halfway between a and b, marked A. The coordinates of this point A are the expected dollar return for contract A, $50,000, and its utility (or expected utility), .65. Contract B is represented in similar fashion by point B; and accepting neither contract, assuring a net gain of zero dollars, is represented by point C lying right on the utility function. Now the diagram shows what we have already discovered: The dollar expectation for A is greater than that for B, and both are greater than zero. The utility for A is less than the utility of C, while the utility of B is greater than that of C.

FIGURE 2-1

The Manager's Utility Function

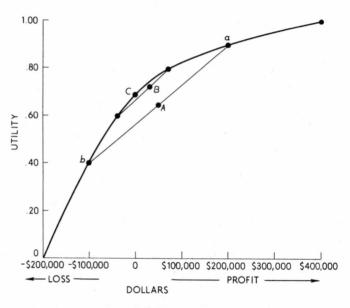

Notice also that if we consider prospects of the form:

a profit of K with probability .50
a loss of K with probability .50

these prospects have zero expected dollar return. As the value of K is increased from zero, the utility of the resulting prospect decreases. Notice also that as K increases the variance of the dollar return increases. Thus we could say that for a given expected dollar return, the manager would prefer the prospect with the smallest variance of the dollar return. This is another characteristic which is described by the term risk aversion. This manager does not like to take chances if he can avoid it, and he seeks certainty in his undertakings.

Other Types of Attitudes

Suppose the results of our utility measuring effort had been different.

The utility function in Figure 2–2 describes the attitudes of a manager who does not feel that the amounts of loss involved in the contracts are such as to put his firm in serious difficulties; thus he is not averse to taking risks if the expected dollar return is positive. For this manager the utility of money is proportional to the amount, and the expected utility is proportional to the expected dollar return. Such a man, if he acts consistently, will want to choose so as to maximize expected dollar return. The analyst need not be concerned about establishing a utility scale, it will differ from the dollar scale only by multiplication by a positive constant and addition of a constant.

FIGURE 2–2

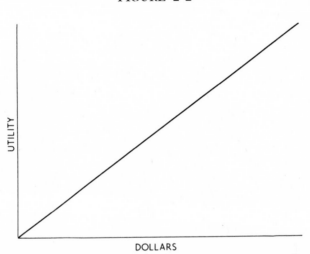

The manager whose utility function appears in Figure 2–3 is a different man entirely. He very much wants to make large profits but is somewhat unconcerned about large losses. He welcomes opportunities to take risks, loves to gamble, and is willing to play long shots. Notice that a prospect promising a profit of D dollars certain, has a lower utility than a prospect having an expected dollar profit of D. For a given expected dollar return, this man prefers the prospect with the highest variance of dollar return.

Finally, Figure 2–4 suggests a sort of utility function for which there is some experimental confirmation. This manager is willing to take gambles involving small amounts of money but not those involving large dollar amounts.

Mistakes

The utility model we have outlined is subtle in its implications, and sometimes mistakes are made in using it. For example:

FIGURE 2-3

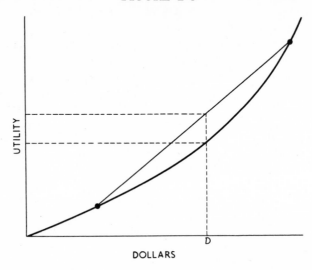

DOLLARS

FIGURE 2-4

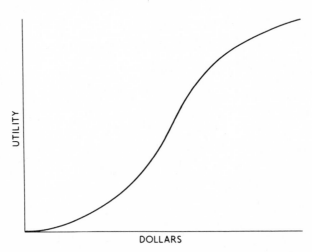

DOLLARS

1. We do not want to fall into the habit of saying that P_1 is preferred to P_2 because $U(P_1) > U(P_2)$. Indeed, it is just the other way around: utilities represent and predict preferences; they do not cause them.

2. We cannot generally say that

$$U(P_1 \text{ and } P_2) = U(P_1) + U(P_2)$$

This will be true only if the utility function is linear. Note that in Figure 2–1 while

$$U(\$400,000) = 1.00$$

$$U(\$200,000) + U(\$200,000) = .90 + .90 = 1.80$$

3. We have so far considered the utility function for particular types of risky actions. We cannot be sure how far these results may be generalized. For example a given manager may be willing to accept contract *B* if it is a venture into the securities market but not if it represents a bet on a horse race.

4. Different people will be described by different utility functions, although we may be able to identify classes of people or firms that may be described by similarly shaped utility functions. We cannot, however, argue that if a gain of $1,000 increases one man's utility by .3 units, while a loss of $1,000 decreases another man's by .2 units, then society will be better off if we take this amount away from the second man and give it to the first. That is, we cannot make interpersonal comparisons of utility.

5. Utility is not an inherent characteristic of people nor of prospects. It is a model which the analyst uses to describe people's preferences or decisions among prospects.

Utility Measurement in Practice

The method of assigning utilities which has been outlined is useful for gaining understanding and insights into the decisions made by managers in the face of risk. One can "explain" decision-making behavior in past decisions and predict consistent choices in future decisions. If the analyst and the manager have the same image or model of a decision and if the manager wishes to act consistently in the sense of the model of his preferences, then the predictions would presumably turn out to be correct. The manager would want to accept the analyst's recommendations. In this sense, the problem of the analyst in dealing with decisions under risk would be "solved." He could provide the manager with consistent recommendations for action in complex decisions, thus relieving the manager for more troublesome problems.

If one could, within the limitations of time and effort imposed by the ongoing affairs of business, measure the manager's utilities, one would clearly find it useful to do so. But what of the difficulties of dealing with an actual managerial situation in this way? Could this actually be done? At best it would appear difficult.

The axioms which lead to this method may be very roughly stated as follows:

1. The decision maker can make a complete and transitive ranking of the outcomes.

2. Any prospect or gamble involving equally desirable outcomes is just as desirable as either outcome by itself.

3. If outcomes A, B, and C are ranked so that A is preferred to B, B is preferred to C, and A is preferred to C, then a gamble exists involving A and C which is just as desirable as B.

4. If A and B are equally desirable then the gamble $pA + (1 - p)C$ is just as desirable as the gamble $pB + (1 - p)C$.

If these axioms hold, then the existence of the utility scale can be shown. The question of interest is whether these axioms do hold in the firm and whether the decision maker can answer questions of the sort indicated previously.

Would the manager be willing to answer the rather large number of questions one would have to ask? Could one put the questions in a meaningful way? Would the manager try to put the analyst off with casual responses, rather than serious consideration? Could he correct the intransitivities and other inconsistencies in his answers? Would his responses be reliable or would distractions lead to errors in the sense of different responses to the same question on different occasions?

Note also that, in presenting the method, we have assumed that the profit and loss aspect of the outcomes alone was relevant. Are there other aspects beside money which have value for him? We have not considered the problem of multiple goals which was raised earlier. If there are other aspects of the outcomes which concern him, then we would have to identify these in order to predict future choices.

Thus there are difficulties, yet it would be unwise to prejudge whether or not one could obtain a useful approximation to a manager's utility function with a reasonable expenditure of time and effort. Two very important points appear, however. First, in many investment decisions choosing so as to maximize expected profit does in fact lead to the same course of action as utility maximization. The importance of utility theory is to suggest which decisions these are and thus which may be treated using the simpler concept of profit. Second, in those decisions where expected profit maximization does not lead to the same conclusions, utility theory is essential to the understanding of existing management policies. Utility theory provides the basis, for example, of an explanation for the widely used corporate policy of diversification in investment decisions. Without utility theory, it is difficult to design management decision systems which reflect the objectives of diversification programs. We consider these two points in turn.

Expected Profit

Possibly the commonest principle of choice in practice suggests that the manager choose the action which maximizes expected profit or minimizes expected loss. We have already seen a case in which this was not satisfactory, but arguments can be given to justify its use in certain other situations. We assume for the present that the dollar consequences of outcomes are the only consequences of concern to the manager.

Suppose we are concerned with a routine decision under risk in a large corporation. The maximum possible profit in the decision is $100 and the maximum possible loss is $50. We are thus interested in the manager's utility function for money in the range from a loss of $50 to a profit of $100. We hypothesize that whatever the shape of his utility function (see Figures 2–1 to 2–4) we will make only neglible errors if we approximate it by a straight line in this range. The smaller the range between minimum and maximum profits in a decision, the better will be a straight line approximation to the utility function. Thus it is argued that over a small range, maximizing expected profit will yield much the same decisions as maximizing utility or expected utility. For this reason, decisions involving moderate dollar consequences can be well understood by maximizing expected profit. As long as the analyst deals with such "small" decisions, he can deal with expected profits and be freed of the necessity for measuring the manager's utility function. The manager in turn is freed from small routine decisions so that he may bring his judgment to bear on large important decisions. Just how to divide decisions into classes in such a way that some may usefully be treated as expected profit maximizing problems while others require utilities cannot be indicated precisely. The judgment and experience of the analyst together with the behavior of the manager must resolve this question in each business situation.

If the cash flows in an investment decision are such that the principle of maximizing expected profit or minimizing expected costs provides a suitable guide, then the logic becomes rather simple. In dealing with futurity calculations of present worth were expressed in forms such as

$$TC(n) = I + \sum_{j=1}^{n} \frac{c_j}{(1+i)^j} - \frac{S_n}{(1+i)^n}$$

Treating the decisions discussed there as decisions under risk is to suppose that predictions of future operating costs and salvage values are in the form of probability distributions. Thus the following predictions are assumed to be available

$f(S_n)$ = density function of the salvage value at the end of n periods of service

$\bar{S}_n$ = expected value of S_n

$g(c_j)$ = density function for the operating cost during the jth period of use

$\bar{c}_j$ = expected value of c_j

It will be noted immediately that since $TC(n)$ is a linear function of these random variables, the expected value of the present worth will be given simply by

$$\overline{TC(n)} = I + \sum_{j=1}^{n} \frac{\bar{c}_j}{(1 + i)^j} - \frac{\bar{S}_n}{(1 + i)^n}$$

This implies clearly that if we wish to use the expectation principle, then we need not be concerned about the density functions involved, but require only the expected costs and salvage values.

Diversification

To illustrate the desirability of a policy of diversification to a manager with an attitude of risk aversion, we consider again the decision maker whose utility function is plotted in Figure 2–1. Suppose this man must choose between contract B which promises a loss of $40,000 with a probability of .40 and a profit of $70,000 with a probability of .60, and a new contract called D. Contract D actually involves taking up two contracts whose outcomes are independent. Each of these two promises a loss of $20,000 with probability .40 and a profit of $35,000 with probability .60. Thus contract D will actually yield a loss of $40,000 with probability .16, a profit of $15,000 with probability .48, and a profit of $70,000 with a probability of .36. The expected profit is the same for contract D as for B, but, of course, the variance of the profit is smaller in the case of D. Thus we would expect the risk averse manager to prefer D. If the utility of $15,000 was .73, then this would be confirmed by the calculation of a utility for D of .73 as opposed to a utility for B of .72. The interesting aspect of contract D is that by diversifying his undertakings between two smaller independent contracts, the decision maker reduces the variance of his profit although no change occurs in the expected profit. To say that he is risk averse is to say that he would prefer not "to put all his eggs in one basket." In Chapter 3 we will return to diversification as an important aspect of capital budgeting decisions.

PROBLEMS

1. The manager whose utility function is shown in Figure 2–1 (see table below) must choose between contract B which promises a loss of $40,000 with probability .40 and a profit of $70,000 with probability .60, and a new contract called D. Contract D actually consists of two contracts, each of which promises a loss of $20,000 with probability .40 and a profit of $35,000 with probability .60. The outcomes of these two contracts making D are independent. What choice would you recommend for the manager?

Utility Table
(Based on Figure 2–1)

Dollars	Utility
− 200,000	0
− 100,000	.40
− 50,000	.58
− 40,000	.60
− 25,000	.64
0	.70
15,000	.73
50,000	.78
70,000	.80
100,000	.83
200,000	.90
400,000	1.00

2. Consider contract *A* of the example in the chapter, which promised a loss of $100,000 with probability .50 and a profit of $200,000 with a probability .50. Suppose four people, each with utility functions like that of Figure 2–1, decide to enter into this contract sharing equally in profits or losses. Suppose further they all use the above probabilities in considering the contract. Show that under these conditions each person's utility will increase. (See table, problem 1.)

3. The manager whose utility function is pictured in Figure 2–1 feels that, although he would not choose contract *A* in the decision discussed in the chapter, if he had the opportunity to accept contract *A* many, many times, it might be more desirable. Show that the utility of taking contract *A* twice is greater than the utility of taking it once.

SUGGESTIONS FOR FURTHER STUDY

GREEN, PAUL. "Risk Attitudes and Chemical Investment Decisions," *Chemical Engineering Progress*, Vol. 59, No. 1 (January, 1963).

MARKOWITZ, HARRY M. *Portfolio Selection, Efficient Diversification of Investments.* New York: John Wiley & Sons, Inc., 1959.

MORRIS, WILLIAM T. *The Analysis of Management Decisions.* Homewood, Ill.: Richard D. Irwin, Inc., 1964.

SCHLAIFER, ROBERT. *Introduction to Statistics for Business Decisions.* New York: McGraw-Hill Book Co., Inc., 1961.

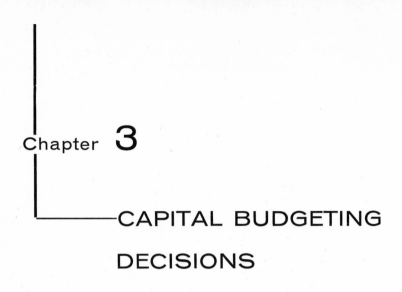

Chapter **3**

CAPITAL BUDGETING

DECISIONS

Investment Programs

WE HAVE SO FAR dealt largely with the choice of one among several mutually exclusive investment proposals. We turn now to the problem of undertaking a program involving numerous investment projects, the sort of program typically undertaken by large firms on an annual basis. Throughout the year investment proposals are generated by the operating divisions of the firm, by its long-range planning group, by its product development group and so on. These proposals are accumulated until, say, once a year a decision is made as to which of them will be funded. To begin the discussion, we consider projects in which no statement of uncertainty is given. This is equivalent to assuming that uncertainty has been suppressed, or that the expectation principle may be used and present worths are to be interpreted as expected values. Later we will return to a consideration of risk in the capital budgeting process.

Capital Rationing

We will sketch two formulations of the problem of allocating scarce funds to candidate projects. The first of these, which stems directly from classical economic theory, involves the use of interest rates interpreted as the cost of capital to the firm. The problem is formulated in terms of the supply and demand of capital from the point of view of the firm. The firm is seen as having opportunities to obtain various amounts of capital from various sources, at prices reflected by interest rates. It is assumed that these interest rates are known, although it may be no simple matter to establish the proper cost of capital obtained from, say, retained earnings. In any case the sources of funds are listed in order of increasing interest rates of cost of capital, and this list is called the capital supply schedule for the firm.

The demand for capital is represented by the projects which are candidates for investment. The problem is greatly simplified if one can assume that the projects are independent. The word "independent" is used here to suggest the condition that the profitability of project A does not depend on whether or not project B is undertaken. In reality, one seldom confronts a group of projects which are strictly independent, and in some cases the dependence is absolute, as in the situation where the undertaking of project A renders project B impossible. This latter condition of dependence, or mutual exclusion, has been discussed in the previous analysis.

The rate of return for a project is defined as that interest rate at which the present worth of the receipts and disbursements is equal to zero. Suppose, for example, the firm invests $11,000 in a project which will have a life of 10 years. The average annual profit from the project is $1,360 and the equipment will have a salvage value of $1,800 at the end of the 10-year life. Trial and error will show that if this stream of receipts and disbursements is discounted at 6 percent, their present worth becomes zero. Thus

$$(\$1,360)(7.360) - \$11,000 + (\$1,800)(.5584) = 0$$

The project is then said to yield a rate of return of 6 percent. Trial and error in conjunction with the interest tables is the common method of determining rates of return.

After the rates of return for all the candidate projects have been determined, the demand schedule for capital may be constructed. This is done simply by listing the candidate projects in order of decreasing rate of return. The solution of the capital budgeting problem is then simple. The two schedules are compared, and one starts at the top of the supply schedule allocating funds to the projects at the top of the demand schedule. This process continues down the two schedules until the point is reached where the rate of return from the next project is less than the cost of capital that would be used to finance it. At this point the process stops, for there is little advantage in undertaking propects which do not earn a return at least equal to the cost of the cheapest funds available to finance them. The firm will, however, wish to undertake all projects that promise a rate of return greater than the cost of their capital, since the excess represents the firm's profit. In economic theory of this sort, no firm passes up an opportunity for profit. The solution to the capital budgeting problem is then to allocate the inexpensive funds from the top of the supply schedule to the projects promising high return at the top of the demand schedule, and to continue this process as long as any possibility for profit remains.

Sources of Funds

After the initial capitalization of the firm, when it becomes a going business, there is often a strong preference for the financing of investment projects out of funds which become available from internal sources. The usual internal sources of funds for the firm are depreciation and retained earnings. Customarily the firm "charges off" depreciation of its productive assets against its current earnings. This results in a flow of cash into the firm, which may then be reinvested in other projects. It is often a policy to "plow back" or retain some of the current earnings, rather than paying all of this money to the stockholders in the form of dividends. A wide variety of policies exist with respect to the portion of current earnings which should be retained for reinvestment.

A number of empirical studies of firm investment seem to indicate a general preference for financing from the inside with the firm's own funds, rather than through debts incurred outside the firm. Associated with this is the obvious result that the volume of investment is directly constrained by the funds available within the firm, or its internal liquidity. Obtaining funds outside the firm is beset with the usual difficulties of interest charges and fixed obligations in the case of bonds, and high financing costs and dilution of control and earnings in the case of common stocks. In addition, management tends to be cautious about debt financing since they themselves find it somewhat less attractive than internal financing. If, for example, an investment made with borrowed funds fails, management may find itself forced into bankruptcy and voted out by the stockholders. If it succeeds, they gain relatively little because they are likely to own only limited amounts of stock themselves. On the other hand, if they finance a project internally through retained earnings, the resultant reduction in dividend payments is of slight consequence to the managers personally.

The Cost of Capital

When the firm is using capital obtained from the sale of common stock, from retained earnings, or from depreciation charges, the proper cost to associate with these funds is a matter of considerable difficulty and disagreement. We will suggest but one possible point of view.

Common Stock. The firm may undertake to market a new issue of common stock in order to finance its major projects or expansion programs. If we neglect, for simplicity, the marketing costs, the firm might well take the cost of funds obtained in this way to be the ratio of estimated annual earnings per share outstanding (without the project) to present market value per share. This ratio is in fact the rate of return which the present stockholders are currently enjoying on their money. From their point of view it is clear that any project which produces a lower rate of return will operate to their disadvantage. Thus, this ratio should be used as the cost of funds obtained from common stock issue, and no project should be undertaken with a lower rate of return.

To illustrate, suppose that a firm presently has 10,000 common shares outstanding, with a market value of $100 per share, and with estimated future earnings (without further expansion) of $12 per share annually. Suppose the firm were to issue an additional 1,000 shares, thus obtaining $100,000 of new equity capital. Suppose further that this new capital were used to finance a project which produced an annual return of $10,000. The firm now has 11,000 shares outstanding with total annual earnings of $130,000. Under these conditions the earnings per share are about $11.82, resulting in a deterioration of the position of the original owners.

Retained Earnings. If a project is to be financed out of earnings retained by the firm, it may plausibly be argued that the same ratio might be used as the cost of capital. That is:

$$\frac{\text{Estimated Earnings per Share without Project}}{\text{Present Market Value per Share}}$$

Again from the stockholders' point of view, it is argued that no funds should be invested in projects promising returns of less than this amount since a better alternative is always open to them. They could always take the funds in dividends and reinvest at the aforementioned rate.

Depreciation Allowance. Funds obtained by the firm through depreciation of its assets may also be treated in this same way. From the owner's point of view, these funds are not essentially different from retained earnings, at least as far as their use is concerned.

Allocating a Fixed Sum

The second formulation of the capital budgeting problem which will be explored involves the allocation of a fixed sum of money among the candidate projects. Often a firm decides to restrict its capital investment to some limited amount, rather than to continue to invest until all profitable opportunities are funded, as was suggested previously. It may be that the firm cannot in fact obtain outside funds at any reasonable cost, or, for a variety of other reasons, the decision may be made to limit investment to those funds which are available internally. The amount of internally available funds depends directly on earnings and dividend policy.

We then consider the problem of allocating a fixed amount of money among a list of possible projects. This problem may be complicated if outlays are to be made in more than one year or accounting period. We will continue to focus our attention only on the present year. Also, difficulties will arise because of discontinuity. That is, there is no assurance that the sum of the investments in any group of projects will exactly equal the fixed amount available. This is likely to be most troublesome when a small number of projects constitute a large portion of the capital budget.

One possibility is to compute the equivalent annual profit for each proposed project using the firm's cost of capital, and then form the ratio of this equivalent annual profit to the total investment required. The projects are then ranked in order of decreasing equivalent annual profit to outlay ratio. Budgeting is accomplished by investing in those projects selected by moving down the list until the fixed sum is exhausted. The use of equivalent annual profit here implies that each project is the first in a program of identically profitable projects extending into the indefinite future. Alternatively we might consider each project as an investment program extending out to some given planning horizon. We could then compute the present worth for each program, and the present worth per dollar of investment. Those programs having the highest present worth per dollar of investment would be selected for funding, until the budget is exhausted.

This problem can be neatly formulated in an integer programming framework as follows

Let:

I_i = the initial investment required by the ith program
P_i = the present worth of the cash flows for program i, assuming all programs extend out to a given planning horizon
x_i = 1 if program i is funded , 0 otherwise
B = total budget available to the firm

The capital budgeting problem is then to maximize the present worth

$$Z = \sum_i x_i P_i$$

subject to the constraint

$$\sum_i x_i I_i \leq B$$

by assigning values to the x_i. Well-developed methods are available for carrying out such solutions. This formulation indicates rather clearly the difficulties to be expected if the programs are interdependent. The present worth for a given program may then depend on which other programs are funded. The function to be maximized can no longer be written as a simple linear function in that case.

Diversification

A firm's attempt to undertake a diversified program of investment is clearly a case in which the desirability of one project is not independent of the other projects which are to be funded. In such a case, one cannot usefully consider single projects but rather "portfolios" or groups of projects. As we have seen, diversification can be understood in terms of risk aversion and the desire to reduce the variability or uncertainty of one's profits. Among the many examples of this is the widespread use of all forms of insurance, which involves the payment of a premium in return for a guarantee against large losses. The insurance companies, by writing a large number of insurance contracts, can maintain a moderate liquid reserve to meet current claims, while making long-term investments with the remainder of their funds. The larger the number of contracts, the smaller the variability in annual claims per contract. The other side of the coin is the position of the insured, who knows that his outlay will be his annual premium and is thus relieved of the uncertainty of possible damaging losses.

Diversification in a firm's capacity investment plans may be aimed at making greater use of some resource which the firm already has in excess. It may, for example, add new products so as to take advantage of existing production facilities, distribution channels, or management skills. These are common motives for diversification moves. Such a policy may, however, bring with it other advantages if the activities or products grouped together by the firm produce returns which are to some degree random and independent. The resulting reduction in the variability of a firm's income is one of the basic strengths of large diversified corporations. They may not be more profitable than small or specialized firms, but their profit is more stable and less uncertain.

This effect in capital budgeting can be illustrated very simply. Suppose a firm is considering a program of investment in two production facilities, involving perhaps two quite different products. The firm has a capital fund to invest of B dollars and has the option of putting any amount into either facility. That is, the firm can undertake either activity at any scale of investment it wishes. It regards the present worth per dollar invested in facility i as a random variable with mean m_i and standard deviation s_i. In the simplest case, these random variables are taken to be independent of one another.

Any program of investment consists of investing some amount x in facility 1 and the remaining $B-x$ in facility 2. The expected present worth from a program is

$$xm_1 + (B - x)m_2$$

and the variance of the present worth, considered as a function of x is

$$\text{Var.}(x) = x^2 s_1^2 + (B - x)^2 s_2^2$$

For illustration we suppose that $m_1 > m_2$ and $s_1 > s_2$. If the firm wished simply to maximize its expected present worth it would invest all of its funds in facility 1, finding no benefit in diversification. If, however, it wished to reduce the variability or uncertainty of its present worth, it would wish to diversity its funds between the two facilities. That is, it would be willing to suffer a reduction in the expected value of its present worth in return for a reduction in the variance. The variance is a quadratic function of x which takes a minimum at the value

$$x = B \frac{s_2^2}{s_1^2 + s_2^2}$$

Thus the firm, depending on its utility function or degree of risk aversion, may wish to select a value of x somewhere between this minimizing value and B. If it does so, it will have an investment program which has the smallest variability in present worth for any given expected value, or the highest expected present worth for any given level of variability.

Capital Budgeting Systems in Practice

Ideally, the firm should have long-range plans for its development in a continual process of formulation and reformulation.[1] Included in these plans would be predictions of the flow of cash into the firm and the firm's cash position at various future times. The plans would also include, as far as possible, estimates of the cash requirements and profitability of projects which might be undertaken in the future. The formulation of these long-range plans then includes the problem of allocating available cash to the candidate projects so as to best achieve the firm's objectives.

In actuality this ideal of long-range plans for the firm's realization and allocation of funds can seldom be achieved with any conviction. Perhaps a commoner formulation of the problem is to view it in terms of the funds available to the firm in the present year or the coming year and the allocation of these funds to the projects which are current opportunities for the firm. Although we will discuss capital budgeting in this way, it is well to remember that the whole process requires considerable advanced planning.

Many projects require a considerable gestation period between the conception and the realization of the project. The firm may also find it necessary to obtain funds from outside sources in order to finance the project, which may itself consume considerable time.

In actuality, decisions as to how to ration funds among the various projects under consideration may be influenced to an important degree by persuasion. People and departments within the firm may actively compete for the funds, each hoping to secure support for some "pet project"

[1]See the explanation of dynamic planning in H. L. Timms, *Introduction to Operations Management* (Irwin Series in Operations Management [Homewood, Ill.: Richard D. Irwin, Inc., 1967]), chap. 5.

or program which will enlarge a particular phase of the firm's operations. It is certain, too, that the provision and allocation of funds are heavily influenced by such factors as the preference of management for a strong cash position, the outlook for business, and the securities markets.

Perhaps of equal importance with these logical considerations discussed in this chapter are the administrative arrangements by which a large firm carries out the capital budgeting functions. The pattern of delegation of the various steps in the process, the difficulties of communication among various organizational units, and the effectiveness with which the delegated activities are coordinated are crucial questions in the design of such systems. These will be considered in Chapter 6.

PROBLEMS

1. A firm has three sources from which it may obtain funds. It can borrow up to $100,000 from a bank at an interest rate of 10 percent, up to $50,000 from a commercial lender at 12 percent, and up to $20,000 from a private investor at 15 percent. No other sources of funds are open to the firm. It has available three investment opportunities. It may invest any amount up to $50,000 in opportunity A with a return of 18 percent, any amount up to $60,000 in opportunity B at 16 percent return, and any amount up to $60,000 in opportunity C with a return of 12 percent. What program of borrowing and investing would you recommend?

2. A firm has developed the following list of projects as current possibilities for investment. All projects are expected to serve for 10 years.

Project	Estimated Annual Profit (before Depreciation)	Investment
A	$1,630	$10,000
B	1,952	12,000
C	1,196	6,000
D	1,416	8,000
E	1,947	11,000
F	4,200	15,000
G	2,147	9,000
H	1,490	10,000

a) Assuming that firm uses a rate of return of 12 percent as its "cost of capital," draw up a capital budget.

b) Draw up a capital budget in which available funds amount to $30,000. Do the same for funds totaling $40,000, $50,000, and $70,000.

SUGGESTIONS FOR FURTHER STUDY

BIERMAN, H., and SMIDT, S. *The Capital Budgeting Decision*. New York: The Macmillan Co., 1960.

SOLOMON, E. (ed.). *The Management of Corporate Capital*. Glencoe, Ill.: The Free Press, 1959.

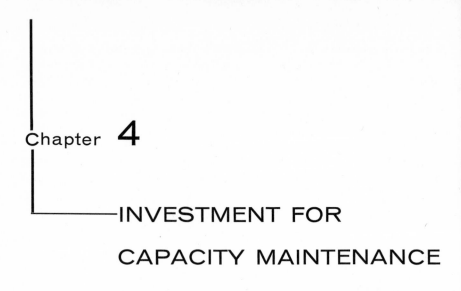

Chapter **4**

INVESTMENT FOR

CAPACITY MAINTENANCE

Maintenance and Expansion of Capacity

SOMETIMES A FIRM makes an investment in production facilities which is primarily aimed at replacing technologically or economically outworn equipment. The demand for the services of the equipment in question is expected to continue for an extended period in the future. The new facilities may involve a technology similar to those they are replacing or the technology may be markedly different. In any case the objective is to maintain the firm's productive capacity at approximately the current level. Other investments involve the deliberate expansion of the firm's capacity, either in its existing lines or in new and diversified products. While some investments designed primarily to replace existing capacity do indeed increase the firm's capability, the distinction is usually clear in terms of the objectives of its capital investment plans.

Whether an investment is for capacity maintenance or capacity expansion the basic principles outlined in the previous chapters apply. Whatever the objective, the investment decision must consider the methods of evaluating the futurity and uncertainty of the cash flows predicted, and the logic of selecting from among a list of proposals remains useful. The two types of investments do, however, differ in some significant ways. Capacity maintenance implies a continuation of an activity in which the firm has considerable experience, has a substantial background of data, and a well-developed structure of operating policy and skill. The prediction that the demand for its output will continue *at least* at a level which will justify replacement of existing capacity is a more conservative and less uncertain prediction than one of expanding demand. Thus an investment for capacity maintenance may be the subject of considerably less uncertainty than one involving expansion of new or existing facilities.

Capacity maintenance investments may well be characterized by a greater degree of interdependence. If a major element of a production process fails, it is clear that replacement is necessary if the entire plant is not to be shut down. On the other hand, plans for expansion may be taken up or not, more or less independently of the conduct of current operations. Thus capacity maintenance investments, being matters of overwhelming necessity, subject to moderate uncertainty, and rather well covered by policy, may become somewhat routinized. Established procedures for evaluation and decision making may permit capacity maintenance investments to be delegated to lower levels in the organization, to require less support, justification, and decision time, and often may not require the attention of top management at all.

Investments for capacity expansion typically arise out of proposals originating in marketing groups, research departments, new product development groups, or long-range planning departments. They involve predictions of increased demand in existing product lines, or potential demands in new areas. They have major implications for the direction in which the firm as a whole wishes to move. They are far more the concern of those who are responsible for overall corporate planning than those who are concerned with the current operations of the firm. In this chapter we consider the formulation of policy for replacement of capacity, while in the following chapter the more difficult problems of expansion policy are introduced.

Replacement Policy

The decision as to the best time to replace a machine has traditionally occupied a major portion of the attention of analysts in the field of management decisions. This is fundamentally due to the frequency with which this decision must be made by most firms, and the significant consequences of the decision. The formulation of a replacement policy plays a major part in the determination of the basic technological and economic progress of the firm. The aggregate of all such replacement policies in use, in turn, becomes a basic determinant of the level of activity of the entire producer goods segment of the economy, which is engaged in the manufacture of production equipment. Thus, when firms begin to defer the replacement of their equipment, the immediate result is a decline in the production of manufacturing equipment, which in turn leads to unemployment, and is often taken as one of the signals that a business recession is under way.

The consequences of an inadequate replacement policy for the firm are potentially disastrous. If the replacement is postponed beyond a reasonable time, the firm may find that its production costs rise, whereas the costs of its competitors who are using more modern equipment are declining. Thus, the firm is no longer able to meet price competition, and finds it impossible either to earn or borrow the funds with which to replace its machines. This is a technological and economic trap from which escape can be made only through the most drastic means.

A secondary reason for the extensive interest in replacement policy is that there are many fundamental assumptions upon which such a policy might be based. Analysts starting from differing basic assumptions have arrived at conclusions which naturally must differ also. Some basic assumptions lead to policies which are relatively easy to apply in practice, while others require the collection of information which is difficult to obtain and the execution of more complex computations. Thus, there has been an important element of controversy over replacement policy, which has stimulated its development, but has perhaps left those who are not specialists in the field a little mystified. We may best avoid pursuing these exchanges of viewpoint by laying out a range of fundamental assumptions upon which replacement policies may be based, and leaving, as always, the choice of assumptions and thus of policy to the analyst. This choice calls for the exercise of his judgment based on an appreciation of the details of the particular situation which he faces.

We will begin with a basic problem of the economic life of an asset and then introduce a variety of possible assumptions which might be used to enrich the analysis. Although the discussion will be carried on in terms of machine replacement, it is not hard to see that the ideas, in fact, apply to any decision involving the termination of one project in favor of another. It is customary to divide assets into two categories: those subject to gradual deterioration over their lives, such as machine tools, and those which suddenly fail, such as light bulbs. In this chapter we discuss only the first category of assets.

Economic Service Life

Let us begin with the problem of economic service life, which can be more precisely stated, "Find the service life for an asset which will minimize the average cost per period of service." Once an asset has been purchased, it is clear that the longer it is used, the more periods of service one has over which to spread the first cost of the asset. The problem of economic service life will only be interesting if there are some other costs which tend to rise with the age of the asset. For most machines, operating cost, maintenance cost, and the like tend to go up as the life of the machine progresses. Thus, there is an economic life where the declining capital recovery cost is offset by the increasing operation and maintenance costs, and the total of these costs is minimized. To show this, let

$$TC(n) = \text{total cost over the life of an asset which is replaced after } n \text{ periods}$$

$$AC(n) = TC(n)/n \text{ average cost per period}$$

$$I = \text{initial investment in the asset}$$

$$c_j = \text{sum of operating and maintenance costs in period } j$$

The problem is simply to choose n so as to minimize $AC(n)$. To make it simple we will assume that the interest rate is taken to be zero, that the asset has no salvage value at any time, that minimizing average cost per period is a reasonable objective, and that

$$c_j \geq c_{j-1} \qquad \text{for } j = 2, 3, \cdots\cdots\cdots$$

This last assumption simply indicates that operation and maintenance costs do not increase with the age of the asset.

In these terms the total cost of an asset kept in service for n years may be written as:

$$TC(n) = I + \sum_{j=1}^{n} c_j$$

and

$$AC(n) = TC(n)/n = \frac{I}{n} + \frac{I}{n}\sum_{j=1}^{n} c_j$$

Now suppose we let N be the value of n which minimizes $AC(n)$. It must be true that

$$AC(N + 1) - AC(N) \geq 0$$

and

$$AC(N - 1) - AC(N) \geq 0$$

Substituting in the first of these conditions for a minimum, the expression for average cost, we have

$$\frac{I}{N+1} + \frac{1}{N+1}\sum_{j=1}^{N+1} c_j - \frac{I}{N} - \frac{1}{N}\sum_{j=1}^{N} c_j \geq 0$$

$$NI - (N+1)I + N\sum_{j=1}^{N+1} c_j - (N+1)\sum_{j=1}^{N} c_j \geq 0$$

$$= I + Nc_{N+1} - \sum_{j=1}^{N} c_j \geq 0$$

$$c_{N+1} \geq \frac{I + \sum_{j=1}^{N} c_j}{N} = AC(N)$$

Performing similar operations with the second of the conditions for a minimum we may obtain the result

$$c_N \leq AC(N)$$

Putting both of these inequalities together yields

$$c_N \leq AC(N) \leq c_{N+1}$$

The ideal replacement policy model would reflect the complex considerations of a firm's replacement problems in detail and thus approach a "best" or optimal policy. Yet at the same time an ideal model would be simple enough for easy data collection, computation, and understanding. Since these two goals are antithetical, the analyst must seek some compromise between them, balancing as he thinks best the two opposing effects.

In examining the models which follow, we will sometimes obtain both analytical solutions and direct evaluations for a range of alternative policies. The analytical solutions are useful for obtaining insights into the sense of policy deduced from the models, but in most current applications, direct evaluations like that of Table 4–1 would be done by a computer. Numerous computer programs for these models are already available, and the interested reader will find it rather easy to develop his own.

TABLE 4–1

n	I/n	$\sum_{j=1}^{n} c_j$	$\frac{1}{n} \sum_{j=1}^{n} c_j$	$AC(n)$
1............	$1,000	$ 50	$ 50	$1,050
2............	500	160	80	580
3............	333	340	113	446
4............	250	600	150	400
5............	200	950	190	390
6............	167	1,400	233	400
7............	143	1,960	280	423

On this basis we may then formulate the following policy: *Replace at the end of any period for which the operation and maintenance costs in the next period exceed the average cost up to the time of replacement. Do not replace as long as the operation and maintenance costs in a period do not exceed the average cost to the end of the period.* If we interpret c_j as the marginal cost of obtaining the service of the machine for period j, given that it has served to the end of period $j - 1$, then this policy will be recognized as an application of a familiar principle. The average cost will come down as long as marginal cost is below it. When marginal cost exceeds average cost, then average cost will begin to rise.

A simple example will illustrate this policy. Suppose a machine can be obtained for an investment of $1,000 and that the pattern of its operating and maintenance costs is predicted as follows:

j	1	2	3	4	5	6	7
c_j	$50	$110	$180	$260	$350	$450	$650

Table 4–1 illustrates a complete set of average cost computations for this machine. In general, it would not be necessary to carry out all of these computations, for a good guess at economic life might lead quickly to an answer which could be shown to satisfy our conditions.

Inspection of the right-hand column will show that the average cost is minimum at the end of five years of service. Thus $N = 5$ and AC (N) = $390 and the conditions previously derived are satisfied.

$$c_N = c_5 = \$350 \le AC(N) = \$390 \le c_{N+1} = c_6 = \$450$$

To restate the policy: *As long as the marginal cost is below the average cost, do not replace. When marginal cost exceeds average cost, then replace.* This analysis might be useful as a basis for replacement policy under the following conditions. Suppose the machine in question is utilized in an activity which is expected to continue for an indefinite period. When this machine is replaced it will be replaced by another which has been predicted to have identical investment and operating costs, and all future machines will have the same characteristics. Then the economic life calculated previously will be the optimal time of service for each machine in this indefinite sequence of machines. Since we assumed that we are planning for a series of identical machines, the best thing to do is to replace every N periods.

If we now modify this analysis by introducing a series of predicted salvage values for the machine at various points in its life, we obtain a slightly different result. If we take S_j to be the salvage value of the machine at the end of the jth period of service, then it can be shown that N must satisfy the following double inequality:

$$C_N + S_{N-1} - S_N \le AC(N) \le c_{N+1} + S_N - S_{N+1}$$

Note here that the marginal cost interpretation also applies since $S_{j+1} - S_j$ is simply the loss in salvage value suffered by extending the life of the asset by one more period. This added to the operating and maintenance costs is the marginal cost.

Replacement Policy Assumptions

The restrictive assumptions made to simplify the foregoing analysis indicate something of the possibilities for alternative bases upon which replacement policies might be based. We will now attempt to establish several important classes of assumptions and describe some of the alternatives within these classes.

1. *Planning Horizon.* By the planning horizon we simply mean the point in time furthest in the future which is considered in the formulation of policy. In some methods of analysis it is convenient to assume an infinite or indefinitely removed planning horizon. Sometimes, while we may not take this assumption too seriously, it may be convenient to use a mathematical method which is consistent with this view of the planning horizon. This assumption is used when we simply are unable to predict when the activity under consideration will be terminated. In other cases it may be clear that the project will have a definite and predictable duration and that the formulation of replacement policy might more realistically be based upon a finite planning horizon.

2. *Technology.* Assumptions with respect to technology refer to the development of the class of machines which are candidates to replace those under study. If we assume that all future machines will be the same as those now in service, then we are saying that there will be no technological progress in the area. However, we may wish to explicitly recognize that machines which may become available in the future are significantly more efficient, reliable, or productive than those now on the market. This assumption leads to the recognition of the phenomenon of obsolescence. Clearly, if the best available machine gets better and better all the time, our decision to replace the machine we now have may be considerably hastened. The difficulty is, of course, to quantify this phenomenon of obsolescence so that it can be applied analytically to the formulation of bases for policy.

3. *Predictions of Cost Patterns over Asset Life.* An infinite variety of predictions might be made of revenue, cost, salvage value, and so on over the life of an asset. Sometimes one wishes to assume that revenue is constant, that costs are nondecreasing, and that salvage value is nonincreasing over the life of a machine. In other cases it will be necessary to take account of a decline in revenue over life. This will determine whether the analysis is directed toward cost minimization or profit maximization. In the analysis which follows we will generally assume that operating and maintenance costs do not decrease with age and that salvage values do not increase with age.[1] That is

---

[1] Cost level and pattern will depend, of course, on how the asset, e.g., a machine tool, will be employed as part of a functional or operating system. Accordingly, the cost estimates for capacity investment decisions (maintenance and expansion) require preliminary design of process and plant systems. This preliminary planning is explained in, respectively, Gerald Nadler, *Work Systems Design: The Ideals Concept* (Irwin Series in Operations Management [Homewood, Ill.: Richard D. Irwin, Inc., 1967]); and Ruddell Reed, Jr., *Plant Location, Layout, and Maintenance* (Irwin Series in Operations Management [Homewood, Ill.: Richard D. Irwin, Inc., 1967]).

$$c_{j+1} \geq c_j \qquad \text{for } j = 1,2,\ldots$$
$$S_{n+1} \leq S_n \qquad \text{for } n = 1,2,\ldots.$$

These assumptions have the effect of assuring that most of the functions we will study will have unique minima.

4. Interest Rate. One may choose to assume an interest rate equal to a zero or nonzero rate. In analyses which contemplate an infinite planning horizon it is necessary to use a nonzero interest rate in order to obtain finite costs.

5. Availability of Capital. One may assume that sufficient capital is available either at no cost or at interest rate, i, to the firm in order to make any investments called for by a replacement policy. On the other hand, one may wish to recognize that capital is limited and must be allocated carefully among alternative investments. Thus, the replacement policy would have to recognize the limited availability of funds. One might wish to introduce explicitly the pattern of capital availability over time, and the costs of obtaining additional capital by various means.

This variety of possible assumptions may suggest a large number of possibilities for developing bases for replacement policy. We will not try to exhaust them all, but rather to exhibit a series of different formulations which may serve to introduce the various approaches which might be made. The reader may develop his own skill as a model builder by deducing policies based on assumptions other than those discussed.

Identical Machines, Interest, and Salvage Value

Suppose we assume that an infinite sequence of identical machines is contemplated and the optimum service life is sought. Assume that the salvage value, S_j, is given, that the interest rate, i, is not zero, and that the operating and maintenance cost are nondecreasing with age of the machine. We now let $TC(n)$ stand for the present worth of all future costs associated with an indefinite sequence of identical machines, each of which is replaced after n years (periods).

$$TC(n) = I + \sum_{j=1}^{n} \frac{c_j}{(1+i)^j} - \frac{S_n}{(1+i)^n} + \frac{I}{(1+i)^n} + \sum_{j=1}^{n} \frac{c_j}{(1+i)^{n+j}}$$
$$- \frac{S_n}{(1+i)^{2n}} + \frac{I}{(1+i)^{2n}} + \sum_{j=1}^{n} \frac{c_j}{(1+i)^{2n+j}} - \frac{S_n}{(1+i)^{3n}} + \cdots\cdots$$

$$TC(n) = \left\{ I + \sum_{j=1}^{n} \frac{c_j}{(1+i)^j} - \frac{S_n}{(1+i)^n} \right\}$$

$$\left\{ 1 + \frac{1}{(1 + i)^n} + \frac{1}{(1 + i)^{2n}} + \cdots \right\}$$

This is a geometric series of the form ar^m where

$$a = I + \sum_{j=1}^{n} \frac{c_j}{(1 + i)^j} - \frac{S_n}{(1 + i)^n} \qquad r = \frac{1}{(1 + i)^n}$$

and

$$S_\infty = \frac{a}{1 - r}$$

Thus

$$TC(n) = S_\infty = \frac{I + \displaystyle\sum_{j=1}^{n} \frac{c_j}{(1 + i)^j} - \frac{S_n}{(1 + i)^n}}{\dfrac{(1 + i)^n - 1}{(1 + i)^n}}$$

Note that this has the following interpretation:

$$P = I + \sum_{j=1}^{n} \frac{c_j}{(1 + i)^j} - \frac{S_n}{(1 + i)^n}$$

is the present worth of all the expenses associated with the first asset.

$$P(1 + i)^n = Q = \text{Future worth of } P \text{ after } n \text{ periods}$$
$$(1 + i)^n - 1 = \text{Interest rate for } n \text{ periods}$$

Thus $TC(n)$ is the amount invested now which is equivalent to an indefinite sequence of payments, Q, at the end of every n periods.

If $N = $ optimal service life, then

$$TC(N + 1) - TC(N) \geq 0 \qquad TC(N - 1) - TC(N) \geq 0$$

If, instead of a present worth basis of comparison, we wished to use an equivalent annual cost basis, it is only necessary to recall that if we let $AC(n)$ stand for the equivalent annual cost given replacement every n years, then

$$AC(n) = TC(n)i$$

It can then be easily shown that the foregoing conditions for N may be written as

$$AC(N) \leq c_{N+1} + S_N(1 + i) - S_{N+1}$$
$$AC(N - 1) \geq c_N + S_{N-1}(1 + i) - S_N$$

This may be directly interpreted as follows: *As long as the average cost is greater than the marginal cost of extending the life of the asset by one additional year, do not replce; as soon as the marginal cost of one additional year's service exceeds the average cost, the asset should be replaced.*

While this principle provides the desired insight into the basic considerations of replacement policy, the actual determination of the optimal policy may be easier to compute by the tabular method used previously.

Example

Consider an indefinite sequence of machines, each of which requires an initial investment of $10,000. The salvage value at the end of year j in the life of a machine is given by

$$5000 - 500(j - 1)$$

and the operating and maintenance costs are given as follows:

j	1	2	3	4	5	6	7	8	9
c_j	$1,000	1,200	1,600	2,000	2,200	2,600	3,000	3,400	3,800

The computations leading to the optimal replacement policy are illustrated in Table 4–2 using an interest rate of 10 percent. It should be noted that, having decided that the best time to replace a machine is some 5 or 10 years in the future, one does not simply forget the problem until that time arrives. The replacement policy decision is reviewed and the calculations redone from time to time, as new information becomes available. As one accumulates the operating and maintenance history on a machine, as the market for used equipment changes, and as new models come on the market, the time for replacement may be reviewed.

TABLE 4–2

n	Col. 1 $I + \sum_{j=1}^{n}\dfrac{c_j}{(1+i)^j}$	Col. 2 $\dfrac{S_n}{(1+i)^n}$	Col. 3 Col. 1 − Col. 2	Col. 4 $\dfrac{i(1+i)^n}{(1+i)^n-1}$	Col. 5 $AC(n) =$ Col. 3 · Col. 4
1........	$10,909	$4,545	$ 6,364	1.10000	$7,000
2........	11,901	3,719	8,182	.57619	4,714
3........	13,103	3,005	10,098	.40211	4,060
4........	14,469	2,391	12,078	.31547	3,810
5........	15,835	1,863	13,972	.26380	3,686
6........	17,303	1,411	15,892	.22961	3,649
7........	18,842	1,026	17,816	.20541	3,660
8........	20,428	700	19,728	.18744	3,698
9........	22,040	424	21,616	.17364	3,753

Improved Candidate for Replacement, Finite Planning Horizon

So far we have assumed that all assets under consideration were identical. It is perhaps more realistic to recognize that often the replacement decision involves an asset now in use and a candidate for replacement which is in some ways better than the present asset. This, of course, reflects the technological progress which is continually under way. The current model of a machine is likely to be more effective than the past models, and one would expect it to be less effective than future models. In most areas this technological progress appears as a combination of gradual advances in effectiveness, together with the occasional technological "breakthrough" which revolutionizes the character of the machines. Similarly, the decision to replace a given asset may involve consideration of a candidate for replacement which is of an entirely different nature altogether. Thus, in considering replacement policy for a fleet of forklift trucks, the decision might involve replacement with conveyors rather than simply newer forklifts.

Let us begin by supposing that a firm now has a machine in use on a process which is expected to terminate at some definite point, T, in the future. After T, the process will be discontinued and the requirement for a machine will cease to exist. Thus we have a finite planning horizon. There is presently on the market a newer machine which is in some ways more effective for the application being considered than the present machine. The problem then is, in view of the finite planning horizon, when, if at all, should the present machine be replaced with the newer one. To simplify the problem, let us further assume that the planning horizon is such that if the newer machine is obtained at any time, it will be retained until time T. Assume also that machines will now be appearing on the market prior to T which are significantly more effective than the one now on the market.

The investment in the present machine, I_o, is taken as its realizable value on the used machinery market at the present time. Let

c_{oj} = operating and maintenance costs for the present machine during the jth additional year of use

s_{oj} = salvage value of the present machine at the end of the jth additional year of use

I_1 = investment required to obtain the newer machine

c_{1j} = operating and maintenance costs for the present machine during the jth year of use

s_{1j} = salvage value of the newer machine at the end of the jth year of use.

Assume that the operating and maintenance costs for both machines are nondecreasing with time and that an interest rate, i, is to be used. The problem may then be posed as that of finding the number of additional years of service, n, from the present machine which will minimize the present worth of all costs over the planning period T. Clearly, if n turns out to be zero, the new machine should be introduced immediately; if it turns out to be T, the newer machine should not be used at all.

We may write the present worth of all costs as a function of n:

$$TC(n) = I_o + \sum_{j=1}^{n} \frac{c_{oj}}{(1+i)^j} - \frac{S_{on}}{(1+i)^n} + \frac{I_1}{(1+i)^n}$$

$$+ \sum_{j=1}^{T-n} \frac{c_{1j}}{(1+i)^{n+j}} - \frac{S_{1T-n}}{(1+i)^T}$$

If we let N stand for the optimal value of n, then as usual N must satisfy the following conditions:

$$TC(N+1) - TC(N) \geq 0 \qquad TC(N-1) - TC(N) \geq 0$$

These conditions lead to the following results:

$$c_{oN+1} + (1+i)S_{oN} - S_{oN+1} \geq I_1 i - \frac{S_{1T-N} - S_{1T-N-1}}{(1+i)^{T-N-1}}$$

$$+ \sum_{j=1}^{T-N} \frac{c_{1j}}{(1+i)^{j-1}} - \sum_{j=1}^{T-N-1} \frac{c_{1j}}{(1+i)^j}$$

and

$$c_{oN} + (1+i)S_{oN-1} - S_{oN} \leq I_1 i - \frac{S_{1T-N+1} - S_{1T-N}}{(1+i)^{T-N}}$$

$$+ \sum_{j=1}^{T-N} \frac{c_{1j}}{(1+i)^j} - \sum_{j=1}^{T-N+1} \frac{c_{1j}}{(1+i)^{j+1}}$$

Interpretation of these leads directly to the following principle: *As long as the cost of one additional year of use for the present machine is less than the savings resulting from postponing the purchase of the new machine one year, do not replace; when the cost of extending the use of the present machine for an additional year exceeds the savings resulting from postponing the purchase of the new machine, then the new machine should be purchased.*

Example

Consider a firm which expects to engage in a certain production activity for eight more years, after which time the activity is to be discontinued. Presently used equipment could be sold immediately for $4,000 ($I_o$). Predicted salvage values and operating costs for this equipment are given in the following table.

j	C_{oj}	S_{oj}
1	$1,600	$3,500
1	2,000	3,000
3	2,200	2,500
4	2,600	2,000
5	3,000	1,500

New equipment is available with the following characteristics: $I_1 =$ $8,000

j	C_{1j}	S_{1j}
1	$ 800	$3,800
2	1,000	3,600
3	1,400	3,400
4	1,800	3,200
5	2,000	3,000
6	2,400	2,800
7	2,800	2,600
8	3,200	2,400

Now suppose we assume that the best pattern of replacement will be to retire the present equipment after n additional years, using the new equipment to complete the eight-year period. In general, one would want to investigate the possibility of using more than one of the new machines within the eight-year period, but we will assume that, for the moment, at most one new machine will be used.

Solving the problem, first using an interest rate of zero, we obtain Table 4–3. If interest is taken at 5 percent, the results are as shown in Table 4–4.

TABLE 4–3

Col. 1	Col. 2	Col. 3	Col. 4
n	$I_o + \sum_{j=1}^{n} C_{oj} - S_{oj}$	$I_1 + \sum_{j=1}^{T-n} c_{1j} - S_{1T-n}$	Col. 2 + Col. 3
0	0	$21,000	$21,000
1	$ 2,100	17,600	19,700
2	4,600	14,600	19,200
3	7,300	12,000	19,300
4	10,400	9,800	20,200
5	13,900	7,800	21,700

Improved Candidate for Replacement, Indefinite Planning Horizon

Now let us reformulate the previous problem with somewhat different assumptions. Consider a present machine in use as before and a newer machine which is taken as the first of an indefinite sequence of identical machines. The problem now falls into two parts: finding the best time to replace the present machine, and determining the economic life of the newer machine once it has been placed in service. Let

TABLE 4-4

n	Col. 1 $I_o + \sum_{j=1}^{n} \dfrac{c_{oj}}{(1+i)^j}$	Col. 2 $\dfrac{S_{on}}{(1+i)^n}$	Col. 3 Col. 1 − Col. 2	Col. 4 $\dfrac{I_1}{(1+i)^n}$	Col. 5 $\sum_{j=1}^{T-n} \dfrac{C_{1j}}{(1+i)^{n+j}}$	Col. 6 $\dfrac{S_{1T-n}}{(1+i)^T}$	Col. 7 Col. 4 + Col. 5 − Col. 6	Col. 8 Col. 3 + Col. 7
0........	0	0	0	$8,000	$11,866	$1,624	$18,242	$18,242
1........	$ 5,524	$3,333	$ 2,191	7,619	9,238	1,760	15,097	17,288
2........	7,338	2,721	4,617	7,256	6,999	1,895	12,360	16,977
3........	9,238	2,159	7,079	6,910	5,119	2,030	9,999	17,078
4........	11,377	1,645	9,732	6,581	3,586	2,165	8,002	17,734
5........	13,728	1,175	12,553	6,268	2,254	2,301	6,221	18,774

n = number of years of additional service required of the present machine

N_1 = optimal service life for the newer machine

$AC(N_1)$ = annual cost of the newer machine based upon replacement with an identical machine every N_1 years

We may then write the present worth of all costs as a function of n in the following form:

$$TC(n) = I_o + \sum_{j=1}^{n} \frac{c_{oj}}{(1+i)^j} - \frac{S_{on}}{(1+i)^n} + \frac{AC_1(N_1)}{i(1+i)^n}$$

where

$$AC_1(N_1) = \left\{ I_1 + \sum_{j=1}^{N_1} \frac{c_{ij}}{(1+i)^j} - \frac{S_{1N_1}}{(1+i)^{N_1}} \right\} \frac{i(1+i)^{N_1}}{(1+i)^{N_1}-1}$$

The optimal service life for the new machine, N_1, may be found by the method presented previously and thus the value of $AC_1(N_1)$ may be computed.

Letting N be the optimal value of n, and using the conditions

$$TC(N+1) - TC(N) \geq 0 \qquad TC(N-1) - TC(N) \geq 0$$

we obtain the following results:

$$c_{oN} + S_{oN-1}(1+i) - S_{oN} \leq AC_1(N_1) \leq c_{oN+1} + S_{oN}(1+i) - S_{oN+1}$$

This then suggests that the present machine should be kept as long as the marginal cost of one additional year of service is less than the annual cost for the newer machine. The present machine should be replaced when the marginal cost of one additional year of service exceeds the average annual cost of the newer machine.

Example

Taking the same problem which was formulated in the previous section, let us now assume an infinite planning horizon. Using an interest rate of 0 percent, Table 4–5 shows that the newer machine should be kept five years. Thus we consider that when the newer machine is installed, it is the first of an indefinite sequence of such machines where a replacement is made every five years. The average annual cost for such a chain of machines is $2,400. In Table 4–6 it is shown that the marginal cost for one year of additional service from the present machine is $2,100. Since this is less than $2,400, it would be wise to keep the present machine for at least one more year. The marginal cost of a second year of additional service from the present machine is, however, $2,500. This leads to the conclusion that the present machine should be kept for

TABLE 4-5

Col. 1	Col. 2	Col. 3
n	$I_1 + \sum_{j=1}^{n} c_{ij} - S_{1n}$	$AC_1(n) = $ Col. 2/n
1................$ 5,000		$5,000
2................ 6,200		3,100
3................ 7,800		2,600
4................ 9,800		2,450
5................ 12,000		2,400
6................ 14,600		2,433
7................ 17,600		2,514
8................ 21,000		2,625

only one more year. The average cost for the present machine is also included in Table 4-6 to show that it is *not* relevant in the decision.

TABLE 4-6

n	$AC_0(n)$	$c_{on} + S_{on-1} - S_{on}$
1...........$2,100		$2,100
2........... 2,300		2,500
3........... 2,433		2,700
4........... 2,600		3,100
5........... 2,780		3,500

TABLE 4-7

n	Col. 1 $\sum_{j=1}^{n} \dfrac{c_{1j}}{(1+i)^j}$	Col. 2 $\dfrac{S_{1n}}{(1+i)^n}$	Col. 3 $I_1 + $ Col. 1 $-$ Col. 2	Col. 4 $AC_1(n)$
1........$ 762	$3,619	$ 5,143	$5,400	
2........ 1,669	3,265	6,404	3,444	
3........ 2,878	2,937	7,941	2,914	
4........ 4,359	2,632	9,727	2,743	
5........ 5,926	2,350	11,576	2,674	
6........ 7,717	2,089	13,628	2,685	
7........ 9,700	1,848	15,852	2,742	
8........ 11,866	1,624	18,242	2,828	

TABLE 4-8

n	c_{on}	S_{on}	$c_{on} + S_{on-1}(1+i) - S_{on}$
0........... 0		$4,000	0
1...........$1,600		3,500	$2,300
2........... 2,000		3,000	2,675
3........... 2,200		2,500	2,850
4........... 2,600		2,000	3,450
5........... 3,000		1,500	3,600

Tables 4-7 and 4-8 show the corresponding calculations when an interest rate of 5 percent is used.

Obsolescence

The previous analysis suggests immediately the following generalization. In actuality, the newer machine under consideration is not the first in an indefinite sequence of identical machines. More likely, continuation of technological progress will place upon the market a whole sequence of machines, each one in some ways more effective than its predecessor. The automobile industry with its custom of yearly model changes is the outstanding example of this phenomenon. If one compares one's automobile with the new models each year, the comparison is less and less favorable as the years pass, for two reasons. The car itself is growing older and thus its operating and maintenance costs are rising in comparison to those of a new car. The new cars may be getting better each year in the sense of having lower operating and maintenance costs than the previous year's model. Thus, the car looks worse and worse, partly because it is getting older and partly because the new models are getting better as time passes. It seems only reasonable that this latter phenomenon, usually called obsolescence, should be taken into consideration in developing a replacement policy.

The greatest obstacle to be overcome here is that of predicting the economic effects of future technological progress in a particular field. As we have suggested, this progress often involves both a gradual long-run improvement of future machines and infrequent dramatic advances which have a revolutionary effect on the technology. The latter class of events is believed by many to be virtually impossible to predict very far in advance. Recognizing the underlying obstacles here, let us illustrate the kind of anlysis which would result for a very simple linear prediction of technological improvement. It must be emphasized that such a linear prediction is only illustrative, and it is in no sense argued that technological progress in any particular area proceeds in this way. Of course, one would expect that a linear prediction would lead to a relatively simple problem of analysis, and this is in fact the case.

To make the analysis very simple, let us ask the question, "What is the economic life of a machine which is one of a technologically developing sequence having a constant rate of improvement over time?" Suppose we assume that any machine in the sequence will require the same initial investment and that no salvage values are involved at any time. We also assume that for any machine its operating and maintenance costs increase linearly with age. For example:

Year of Use	Operating Cost
1	First-year cost
2	First-year cost $+ a$
3	First-year cost $+ 2a$
4	First-year cost $+ 3a$
.	. . .
j	First-year cost $+ (j - 1)a$

We may now reflect the assumptions about obsolescence in the statement that the first-year operating cost of a machine decreases in a linear fashion with calendar time (years).

Thus:

Time of Purchase (Manufacture)	First-Year Operating Cost
Beginning of year 1.............c	
Beginning of year 2.............$c - b$	
Beginning of year 3.............$c - 2b$	
Beginning of year 4.............$c - 3b$	
. . . . .	
. . . .	
. . . .	
Beginning of year k.............$c - (k - 1)b$	

In general, then, the operating cost for the jth year of use of a machine which was purchased new at the beginning of year k is given by

$$c + (j - 1)a - (k - 1)b$$

It should be emphasized again that this prediction is only illustrative.

Suppose we wish to establish a policy of replacing this class of machines every n years with the best model that is then available on the market. It should be noted that it is not necessarily clear at the outset that it will be optimal in any sense to have n be a constant; however, this will be established as the analysis goes on. We seek the value of n, say N, which will minimize the following present worth:

$$TC(n) = I + \sum_{j=1}^{n} \frac{c + (j - 1)a}{(1 + i)^j} + \frac{I}{(1 + i)^n} + \sum_{j=1}^{n} \frac{c + (j - 1)a - nb}{(1 + i)^{n+j}}$$

$$+ \frac{I}{(1 + i)^{2n}} + \sum_{j=1}^{n} \frac{c + (j - 1)a - 2nb}{(1 + i)^{2n+j}} + \frac{I}{(1 + i)^{3n}} + \cdots$$

This reduces to

$$TC(n) = \left\{ I + \sum_{j=1}^{n} \frac{c + (j - 1)a}{(1 + i)^j} \right\} \frac{(1 + i)^n}{(1 + i)^n - 1} - \sum_{k=1}^{\infty} \sum_{j=1}^{n} \frac{knb}{(1 + i)^{kn+j}}$$

This may be expressed as an annual cost using the relation

$$TC(n)i = AC(n)$$

yielding

$$AC(n) = \left\{ I + \sum_{j=1}^{n} \frac{c + (j - 1)a}{(1 + i)^j} \right\} \frac{i(1 + i)^n}{(1 + i)^n - 1} - \left\{ \sum_{k=1}^{\infty} \sum_{j=1}^{n} \frac{knb}{(1 + i)^{kn+j}} \right\} i$$

The usual method of solving this problem is to substitute for it another problem which can be shown to have the same solution. The basis for this substitution is the following argument. The annual operating cost of a machine may be thought of as being composed of two parts. The first part is what we have already designated as annual operating cost in the usual sense, using the expression

$$c + (j - 1)a$$

for the first machine. In addition one might argue that by keeping a machine, rather than replacing it with the best model then available, one is in fact giving up the opportunity to realize the savings in operating cost which result from technological advance. Thus it is argued that the operating costs of the first machine increase not only with age, but in terms of opportunities forgone for the realization of lower operating costs through replacement. On the basis of this opportunity cost argument, the operating costs and the opportunity (obsolescence) costs for the first machine may be expressed as

$$c + (j - 1)(a + b)$$

It is further argued that the problem of finding the economic service life for an indefinite sequence of identical machines, whose costs behave in this way, will have a solution which is also the solution to the original problem which we posed. Although this can be proved its validity is roughly suggested in the following example.

Thus we are led to pose the substitute problem of finding the value of n, say N, which will minimize the present worth given by

$$TC(n) = \left\{ I + \sum_{j=1}^{n} \frac{c + (j - 1)(a + b)}{(1 + i)^j} \right\} \frac{(1 + i)^n}{(1 + i)^n - 1}$$

This may be expressed in annual cost form as

$$AC(n) = \left\{ I + \sum_{j=1}^{n} \frac{c + (j - 1)(a + b)}{(1 + i)^j} \right\} \frac{i(1 + i)^n}{(1 + i)^n - 1}$$

Based upon our previous analysis, we can state immediately that the value of n we seek must satisfy the relations

$$AC(N) \leq c + N(a + b) \qquad AC(N - 1) \geq c + (N - 1)(a + b)$$

This value of N is thus the basis for an optimal replacement policy under the conditions of linearly increasing operating costs and linear technological advancement. Note that, in the substitute problem, the optimality of a constant N has been previously established. Given that the substitute problem yields a solution to the original problem, then it follows that constant N is optimal for the original problem also.

Example

Consider a technologically developing sequence of machines, each of which will require an initial investment of $10,000, and will have no salvage value at any time. Suppose that the operating and maintenance costs for the jth year of a machine purchased at the beginning of year k are given by

$$1,000 + (j - 1)(190) - (k - 1)(10)$$

That is: $a = \$190$ and $b = \$10$. We are interested in finding an optimal replacement policy. Let us make the additional simplifying assumption that the interest rate is zero.

As suggested previously, we formulate the substitute problem of finding the economic life for an indefinite sequence of machines for which

$$I = \$10,000$$
$$c_j = 1,000 + (j - 1)(200)$$
$$S_j = 0, \text{ for all } j$$

Solving the substitute problem by the usual tabular method we obtain Table 4–9. For a solution we have $N = 10$ years, which is also taken to be the solution to the original problem. It should be noted that the annual cost for 10 years does not apply to the original problem.

As a check on the validity of the substitute problem let us compute the answer directly. Consider a planning horizon of 30 years. Suppose we were to replace every five years, thus utilizing six machines over the 30-year period. The first of these machines would have operating costs of $1,000, $1,190, $1,380, $1,570, and $1,760 respectively in the five years of its use. The average of these costs is $1,380, and the annual cost of investment recovery is $2,000, yielding an average annual cost of $3,380. The second machine, which is purchased at the beginning of year six, has operating costs of $950, $1,140, $1,330, $1,520, and $1,710 in the respective years of its use. For the second machine the average annual cost turns out to be $3,330. The average annual cost for each of the six machines is as follows:

Machine Number	Purchased at Beginning of Year	Average Annual Cost
1	1	$3,380
2	6	3,330
3	11	3,280
4	16	3,230
5	21	3,180
6	26	3,130

TABLE 4-9

n	I/n	c_j	$\displaystyle\sum_{j=1}^{n}\frac{c_j}{n}$	$AC(n)$
1........	$10,000	$1,000	$1,000	$11,000
2........	5,000	1,200	1,100	6,100
3........	3,333	1,400	1,200	4,533
4........	2,500	1,600	1,300	3,800
5........	2,000	1,800	1,400	3,400
6........	1,667	2,000	1,500	3,167
7........	1,429	2,200	1,600	3,029
8........	1,250	2,400	1,700	2,950
9........	1,111	2,600	1,800	2,911
10........	1,000	2,800	1,900	2,900
11........	909	3,000	2,000	2,909
12........	833	3,200	2,100	2,933
13........	770	3,400	2,200	2,970
14........	714	3,600	2,300	3,014
15........	667	3,800	2,400	3,067

Now the grand average of these annual costs can easily be shown to be $3,255.

Now consider exactly the same computations based on a 10-year replacement period. The results are

Machine Number	Purchased at Beginning of Year	Average Annual Cost
1...............	1	$2,855
2...............	11	2,755
3...............	21	2,655

The grand average of these costs is $2,755.

Repeating the process for a 15-year replacement period we obtain:

Machine Number	Purchased at Beginning of Year	Average Annual Cost
1...............	1	$2,997
2...............	16	2,847

Here the grand average is $2,922.

Let us now compare the annual costs obtained in the solution of the original problem with those obtained in the solution of the substitute problem.

Replacement Period	Annual Cost from Substitute Problem	Annual Cost from Original Problem	Difference
5 yrs.............	$3,400	$3,255	$145
10..............	2,900	2,755	145
15..............	3,067	2,922	145

These computations are perhaps sufficient to suggest that we are dealing with two functions of n which differ only by a constant. It follows then that both functions must take a minimum for the same value of n. Thus, the solution of the substitute problem must also be the solution to the original problem.

The solution to the substitute problem using an interest rate of 6 percent is shown in Table 4-10.

General Replacement Model

At this point it is possible to generalize our replacement model to include technological changes which might be reflected not only in the pattern of operating and maintenance costs but also in changes in initial investment and the pattern of salvage values. Under these conditions it may be that the replacement interval would change as well.

Let

I_t = initial investment in a machine purchased at the end of period t

c_{tj} = operation and maintenance costs for the jth year of a machine purchased at the end of period t

S_{tj} = salvage value at the end of the jth year of use for a machine purchased at the end of period t

N_k = life of the kth machine in the sequence of replacements

We would then have a generalized present worth function which might be written

$$TC(N_1, N_2, \cdots, N_k, \cdots) = I_o + \sum_{j=1}^{N_1} \frac{c_{0j}}{(1+i)^j}$$

$$- \frac{S_{0N_1}}{(1+i)^{N_1}} + \frac{I_{N_1}}{(1+i)^{N_1}} + \sum_{j=1}^{N_2} \frac{c_{N_1 j}}{(1+i)^{N_1+j}}$$

$$- \frac{S_{N_1 N_2}}{(1+i)^{N_1+N_2}} + \frac{I_{N_2}}{(1+i)^{N_1+N_2}} + \sum_{j=1}^{N_2} \frac{c_{N^2 j}}{(1+i)^{N_1+N_2+j}} - \cdots$$

This function may be the sum of an infinite series if the planning horizon is infinite, otherwise it may be carried out to a finite planning horizon. While it is perfectly general, it suffers from the usual difficulty of requiring some very troublesome predictions. It is not possible to write a general solution for it in any interesting form. Further, there are good practical reasons suggested by the previous example for questioning the advantage of the additional detail and expense it would require. It does, however, suggest some of the range of possible bases which one might use in developing a replacement policy. One might do well, however,

TABLE 4-10

Col. 1	Col. 2	Col. 3	Col. 4	Col. 5	Col. 6	Col. 7
n	$\dfrac{c_j}{(1+i)^j}$	$\displaystyle\sum_{j=1}^{n} \dfrac{c_j}{(1+i)^j}$	$\dfrac{i(1+i)^n}{(1+i)^n-1}$	$Col.\ 3 \cdot Col.\ 4$	$I \cdot Col.\ 4$	$AC(n) =$ $Col.\ 5 + Col.\ 6$
1	$ 943.40	$ 943.40	1.06000	$1,000.00	$10,600.00	$11,600.00
2	1,068.00	2,011.40	.54544	1,097.10	5,454.40	6,551.50
3	1,175.44	3,186.84	.37411	1,192.23	3,741.10	4,933.33
4	1,267.36	4,454.20	.28859	1,285.44	2,885.90	4,171.34
5	1,345.14	5,799.34	.23740	1,376.76	2,374.00	3,750.76
6	1,410.00	7,209.34	.20336	1,466.09	2,033.60	3,499.69
7	1,463.22	8,672.56	.17914	1,553.60	1,791.40	3,345.00
8	1,505.76	10,178.32	.16104	1,639.12	1,610.40	3,249.52
9	1,538.94	11,717.26	.14702	1,722.67	1,470.20	3,192.87
10	1,563.52	13,280.78	.13587	1,804.46	1,358.70	3,163.16
11	1,580.40	14,861.18	.12679	1,884.25	1,267.90	3,152.15
12	1,590.40	16,451.58	.11928	1,962.34	1,192.80	3,155.14
13	1,593.92	18,045.50	.11296	2,038.42	1,129.60	3,168.02

to keep in mind that the data for many complex replacement models are highly speculative. A detailed, refined replacement model may be little better than a simple one if the major source of error is unreliable data.

PROBLEMS

1. A firm is presently using a machine which has a market value of $8,000 to do a specialized production job. The requirement for this operation is expected to last only six more years after which it will no longer be done. The predicted costs and salvage values for the present machine are

Year	1	2	3	4	5
Operating cost	$1,000	$1,200	$1,400	$1,800	$2,300
Salvage value	$5,000	$4,500	$4,000	$3,300	$2,500

A new machine has been developed which can be purchased for $12,000 and has the following predicted cost performance:

Year	1	2	3	4	5	6
Operating cost	$ 500	$ 700	$ 900	$1,200	$1,500	$1,900
Salvage value	$11,000	$10,500	$10,000	$9,500	$8,500	$7,500

a) If interest is at 0 percent, when should the new machine be purchased?
b) When, if interest is at 5 percent?

2. For heavy milling jobs a firm uses two mills which were purchased in 1920 at a cost of $2,500 each. They may be sold on the present market for $1,500 each, and their resale value is expected to decline at the rate of about 10 percent per year in the future. The firm is considering replacing these with a single modern machine which will cost $150,000 (installed) and will last up to 20 years. The salvage value of this machine is expected to decline by an equal amount each year to a level of $30,000 at the end of 20 years. Other relevant costs are as follows:

Annual Costs	Old Machines (Total for both)	New Machine
Direct Labor	$33,000	$13,000
Indirect labor	4,000	1,200
Maintenance	5,000	2,000
Tooling costs	0	4,000
Power consumption	3,000	4,500

If the firm uses an interest rate of 6 percent, what is its best choice at this point?

3. Find the optimal replacement interval for machines which require an initial investment of $5,000, have no salvage value, and have annual operating costs given by

$$c_j = 800 + 80(j - 1)$$

The effects of obsolescence are reflected in a decline in the first year operating cost of each year's new model by $120. Interest is 8 percent.

SUGGESTIONS FOR FURTHER STUDY

DEAN, BURTON V. "Replacement Theory, *Progress in Operations Research* (ed. R. L. ACKOFF), Vol. I. New York: John Wiley and Sons, Inc., 1961.

MAYER, RAYMOND R. "Problems in the Application of Replacement Theory," *Management Science,* Vol. 6, No. 3 (April, 1960).

REISMAN, ARNOLD, and BUFFA, ELLWOOD S. "A General Model for Investment Policy," *Management Science,* Vol. 8, No. 3 (April, 1962).

TERBORGH, GEORGE. *Dynamic Equipment Policy.* New York: McGraw-Hill Book Co., Inc., 1949.

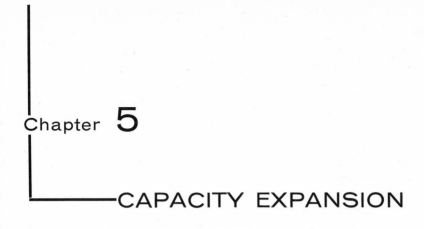

Chapter 5

CAPACITY EXPANSION

Types of Expansion

WHEN A FIRM experiences a growing demand for its output and makes investments aimed at increasing its capacity in these existing lines of activity, the outlays are called induced investments. A feedback loop senses the firm's output, predicts future demand, and management tries to follow the indicated changes with plant capacity in an effective way. Induced investments usually rest upon a sound base of experience and operating policy which moderate to some extent their risk. When, on the other hand, the firm diversifies into new lines of activity, the capital investments involved are referred to as autonomous investments. As compared with induced investments, they are likely to involve more uncertainty, both because of the firm's lack of relevant experience and the more difficult forecasting problems which may be involved. While the basic principles needed to understand the two types are the same, there are special difficulties associated with each.

Induced Investment

The simplest feedback theory of how induced investment takes place is called the acceleration principle. This principle holds that the rate at which a firm invests in new, as opposed to replacement equipment, is a linear function of the rate of change of output. Suppose a firm has a capacity of 100,000 units of output each year, and is operating at that capacity. Assuming that the only way to increase output is to add more capacity, then, as demand increases, capacity must be increased in direct proportion. An illustrative history is shown below:

81

Year	Demand	Required Capacity	Investment in New Capacity
1............100,000		100,000	0
2............100,000		100,000	0
3............110,000		110,000	10,000
4............110,000		110,000	0
5............120,000		120,000	10,000
6............140,000		140,000	20,000

The acceleration principle assumes that capacity is well defined and that, when it is reached, such alternatives as overtime, subcontracting, and back ordering are not available. It purports to explain only new investment or net investment. One must still look for an explanation of the firm's investment for replacement purposes. The principle also assumes that the firm is able to obtain the funds to finance the indicated expansion.

When demand is constant the firm's investment may be confined to replacement of its existing capacity, although if this was not being fully utilized the firm might actually neglect replacement. While the acceleration principle provides a first indication, effective implementation of an expansion program requires considerably greater insight.

Alternatives to Capacity Expansion

Capacity is not a particularly well-defined concept in most firms. There is a gradual growth in unfilled orders and overtime, shifts are added, and any "slack" or hidden capacity comes into use. Thus management has several alternatives to capacity expansion. It can use inventories as a demand buffer, to insulate to some extent the steady operation of production facilities from changes in the market. Negative inventories or back orders are a useful means of meeting what appear to be temporary increases in demand. The major difficulty with using negative inventory in this way is that the "cost" of such a policy is most difficult for management to evaluate and thus use reasonably. As unfilled orders increase, customers may become impatient and go elsewhere rather than accept distant delivery dates. Just how much business is lost in this way is difficult to predict, thus it is sometimes impossible to decide how high negative inventories should be permitted to grow. In other cases delays in delivery may have quite a different effect. Customers who order regularly, finding the lead time for delivery growing longer, increase their order rates. Effectively they put their orders in earlier in the face of the extended delivery dates. Thus the firm experiences a new surge in demand which further increases its negative inventories. If it now adds to its capacity, deliveries may begin to catch up with demand. Customers, finding deliveries improved, stop ordering early and work off the inventories they are beginning to accumulate. Thus the firm experiences a very severe drop in demand and finds itself with considerable excess capacity.

The capacity of existing facilities can also be extended by working overtime or expanding the work force. Overtime, though expensive, is usually chosen first because its effects are not as irreversible. The cost of adding a new employee and the ill will generated by laying him off tend to restrict work force changes to relatively permanent increases in demand. Sometimes capacity can be expanded by subcontracting part of the production process to others and effectively buying rather than making some of the required output.[1] The general management decision problem of what mix of inventory, overtime, work force expansion, and subcontracting to use in any situation is a most difficult one to bring under careful analysis. Yet all are used, largely because their reversibility outweighs their expense, as means of damping out the changes in plant capacity in the face of varying demand.[2]

The basic problem is, of course, how to forecast effectively the future movements of demand. If an increase is believed to be permanent, then it is economically preferable to increase capacity, rather than the more costly alternatives of overtime or inventories. Yet if the increase in demand is short lived, it is far better not to be caught with new capacity which is now idle. Thus the problem is to make a forecast, assess the uncertainty of the forecast, and then select the most economic mix of capacity expansion and its alternatives in the face of this uncertainty. We will shortly make an explicit formulation of a simplified version of this decision problem.

There is some considerable evidence that the forecasting techniques used in many firms consist essentially of linear projections of past activity. Such forecasting methods imply, in terms of our feedback analogy, that when demand changes from a constant level to an increasing trend, the prediction of future demand will tend to lag somewhat behind the de-

---

[1]The nature of the "make-or-buy" decision is explained in Wilbur B. England, *The Purchasing System* (Irwin Series in Operations Management [Homewood, Ill.: Richard D. Irwin, Inc., 1967]), chap. 3. However, the make-or-buy decision process is a dynamic one in the sense that it must be integrated with the capacity decision process as explained here, thus operating as a decision system, with feedback between the two decision processes. An item can switch from the "make" to the "buy" category and vice versa, as capacity conditions change through time.

[2]Variation in demand about a relatively stable level of demand, e.g., as occurs with cyclical changes in gross national product, normally will be accommodated without adding to physical capacity. A secular increase in demand calls for decisions on when, in the firm's long-range plans, an addition to capacity (an expansion) is appropriate. Shifts in the level of demand, on the other hand, may be caused by neither cyclical nor secular influences, but rather by competitive action (often quite sudden), as when a revolutionary design change in a product lures a large percent of competitors' shares of the market away from them.

velopment of actual demand. Capacity expansion, based on linear extrapolation, will thus tend to fall behind demand. When, however, demand changes from an upward growth to a stable level or enters a period of decline, the lag of the forecast will tend to leave the firm with excess capacity. Thus, in this situation, linear projections are not what is wanted and the feedback system needs to be based on changes in the rate of change in demand, or the second derivative of demand.

The Indivisibility of Assets

A further complication in attempting to match plant capacity with demand arises from the "lumpiness" of capital assets. They can be obtained in various sizes, but are not generally infinitely divisible. New capacity thus tends to become available in increments such as a new plant, a department, a production line, a blast furnace, or a machine tool. Even in the face of a steadily rising demand there is a problem of the size and timing of these lumpy additions to capacity. A capital asset tends to yield its lowest cost per unit of output when fully utilized. This permits spreading the fixed costs over the maximum number of units of production. Thus on the one hand there are advantages to postponing the addition of new capacity until demand has risen to the point that it can be rather fully used. Opposed to these are advantages arising from early additions to capacity in order to avoid the more costly alternatives of overtime, work force expansion, or negative inventories. Earlier introduction of new capacity also prepares the firm for unforeseen increases in demand, while postponing it allows the accumulation of more information on which to base predictions of future demand. Postponing the acquisition of new capacity may allow the firm to obtain equipment which has undergone technological improvements; while obtaining new equipment immediately permits it to have the maximum benefit from the current technology.

If all these factors were to be considered at once, the problem of capacity expansion planning would be very complex indeed. Given an extended but uncertain forecast of demand one would have to decide the timing and size of capacity increments to be made. This decision might include consideration of both futurity and uncertainty, as well as possible technological developments. Because of the difficulty of such an analysis it is seldom explicitly done in practice. We will shortly illustrate with a simpler example the relatively near-term planning horizon used in most industrial situations. The problem can become even more complex since capacity utilization depends on production levels, inventory levels, overtime policy and the size of the work force as well. Decisions about all of these should ideally be made within the context of capacity expansion planning.

Autonomous Investment

A move into a new product line may, as has been suggested, involve greater uncertainty than the expansion of existing lines. The alternatives to capacity expansion, at least at the outset, are not so readily available. The minimum investment to enter may be rather large. The problems of forecasting which form the basis for tracking demand with capacity may also be magnified.

A new product often seems to experience the sort of growth pattern suggested in Figure 5–1.[3] When the product is introduced its sales grow

FIGURE 5–1

Growth in Demand for a New Product

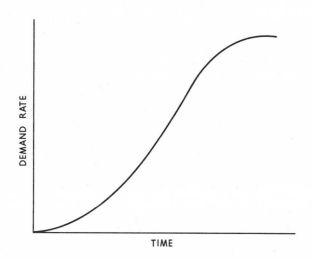

slowly at first, but at an increasing rate. It reaches a period of sustained growth during which sales climb steadily at a rather high rate. Eventually the market becomes saturated or fully covered, and this growth rate declines. Sales stabilize at a constant level or perhaps even decline. In such a situation, forecasts based on a linear extrapolation of past sales serve management badly. In the early stages the firm finds itself with too little capacity. The firm cannot satisfy the demand and as a result some of it may be lost. As capacity increases through plant expansion, sales also increase but the backlog of orders may tend to remain constant. Delays in bringing new capacity into operation coupled with the lags of the linear forecasting technique keep capacity from catching

[3]For an explanation of the growth pattern of new products, see Lewis N. Goslin, *The Product Planning System* (Irwin Series in Operations Management [Homewood, Ill.: Richard D. Irwin, Inc., 1967]), chap. 1.

up with demand during this period of steady growth. As saturation is approached, the forecasting technique is late in detecting the change in growth rate and new capacity is brought into operation after sales have begun to level off. The firm may be left with excess capacity, no backlog of orders, and perhaps even excessive inventories. These difficulties emphasize the importance of forecasting methods and the problem of responding to uncertainty. A specific illustration of this latter problem may be useful.

Capacity Determination under Risk

A typical and important problem in the planning of production facilities is to decide on how many machines will be needed by a plant, or in this case, by a department. We have in mind a typical processing department which will contain similar machines and through which a variety of products may pass. The considerations involved in this decision are obvious. One wants to know the capacity of the type of machine being considered and the production which will be programmed for the department. Then the decision is a simple matter of planning enough machines to carry out the program, or simply matching "supply" and "demand," "capacity" and "load." The trick is to accurately predict the capacity of the machines and the magnitude of the production program. For purposes of discussion let us suggest two rather different approaches or strategies in rationalizing this decision. The approach which may typify much actual practice today treats the decision as one under assumed certainty. We will compare this with an analysis of the decision as one under conditions of risk.[4]

In this example the reader may wish to imagine two groups of analysts studying the problem independently. One group suppresses the risk and deals with the problem as one under assumed certainty. They do this, we will suppose, using a variant of the most probable future principle. Their behavior might be described as suppressing all the variability in their data and using only the mean or average values.

The other group, one might imagine, treats the risk explicitly but assumes for analytical purposes that the utility function of their firm is approximately linear in the relevant region.

Since managerial judgment would undoubtedly enter the decision after each group had made their recommendations to their respective managements, it is difficult to say what the ultimate decision might be in either case. We can, however, show that the analysts themselves reach rather different recommendations.

[4]For an explanation of the final determination of the number of machines to install for plant layout purposes, given the long-range capacity, capital budget, and the resulting capital *structure* plans explained here, see Ruddell Reed, Jr., *Plant Location, Layout, and Maintenance* (Irwin Series in Operations Management [Homewood, Ill.: Richard D. Irwin, Inc., 1967]), chap. 5.

Assumed Certainty

Perhaps it is typical of many instances of this problem that the analyst looks for the following kind of information:

T_{ij} = mean performance time for operation i on product j, measured in hours per unit of product

D_j = mean demand for product j measured in units per production period

H = number of hours in a production period

$\bar{E}$ = mean effectiveness factor; a decimal taking into account the usual personal allowances, machine downtime, material shortages, scrapped production, etc.

Having consulted the time study department, the sales department, and various other sources for these average values, the analyst then performs the following simple calculation. The mean number of machines required by the department is given by

$$\bar{M} = \sum_i \sum_j \frac{T_{ij}\bar{D}_j}{\bar{E}H}$$

where the summation is over products and operations within the department.

This is a fairly typical approach. Note, however, that even the data required here may be difficult to get in an actual situation, and additional simplifications may have to be made, leading eventually to nothing much more than a professional guess. The mathematical model is simple enough for everyone to use and understand. It represents the kind of calculation which most managements seem to find acceptable. The analyst inevitably feels a certain uneasiness at the gross oversimplifications which it involves. He well knows that performance times vary considerably, as any time study sheet clearly shows. Estimates of production demand in most instances are subject to important errors. The events represented by the effectiveness factor also exhibit wide variation. For example, the scrap rate for a process, even when it is in control in the statistical sense, varies to an important extent.[5] Let us assume for the moment that we can obtain data on all these kinds of variation. These data provide the basis for treating the problem as a decision under risk.

Risk

The basic notions associated with this approach are as follows. If the performance times, demands, and effectiveness factors are subject to

---

[5]For an explanation of the determination of process probability, see Robert B. Fetter, *The Quality Control System* (Irwin Series in Operations Management [Homewood, Ill.: Richard D. Irwin, Inc., 1967]), chap. 3. For an explanation of the treatment of scrap loss in determining machine requirements for plant layout purposes, see Ruddell Reed, Jr., *Plant Location, Layout and Maintenance* (Irwin Series in Operations Management [Homewood, Ill.: Richard D. Irwin, Inc., 1967]), chap. 5.

variation, then the actual number of machines required will itself be subject to variation. Realistically then, the management problem is to decide what number of machines should be installed to best meet this varying requirement. The result will be that, in general, there will be periods in which more machines are available than are required, and also periods in which fewer machines are available than are required.

The manager must weigh these consequences, recognizing that, as the number of machines is increased, the chance of having insufficient facilities will decrease, but the chance of having excess capacity increases. This leads to the tactical problem of measuring the costs of these events.

Tactically, also, the problem of describing the variation in the data must be faced. In order to exhibit an initial model let us assume that performance times, demands, and effectiveness factors are random variables which may be described by probability distributions. Thus let

$$f(T_{ij}) = \text{probability distribution of } T_{ij}$$
$$g(D_j) = \text{probability distribution of } D_j$$
$$h(E) = \text{probability distribution of } E$$

We assume that H is fixed by policy and is not subject to important variation. The validity of these assumptions is the subject of much familiar debate. For example, there has been extensive discussion as to whether performance times on man-paced operations can be described by simple probability distributions. If one uses the techniques of inferential statistics to forecast demand, then the resulting forecasts are subject to errors which may be modeled by probability distributions. The effectiveness factor may include such items as machine delays and scrap production, which are often described by the analyst in probabilistic terms. Clearly, if these valuables are taken to be random variables, then the required number of machines, m, will itself be a random variable. Thus

$$f(m) = \alpha [f(T_{ij}), g(D_j), h(E)]$$

The tactical problem of finding the probability distribution of m may be approached in several ways. If the forgoing distributions are taken to be of analytically known form, then there are analytic methods for obtaining the distribution of m. If, however, the forms are not obtained, one might use the Monte Carlo method for obtaining an estimate of the distribution of m. This step can be a very difficult one in actual practice. To develop a model for the decision one might proceed somewhat as follows. Suppose the following data are on hand:

$$f(m) = \text{probability distribution of actual}$$
$$\text{number of machines required in}$$
$$\text{a period}$$
$$C_1 = \text{fixed charges per machine per period}$$

Considerable simplification of the model results if we assume that any production which cannot be completed during the regular production period is completed on overtime or by subcontracting. This avoids the mathematically difficult problem of accounting for production requirements which are carried forward from one period to the next. Assume for the moment that overtime is chosen. Let

$$C_2 = \text{cost penalty (excess over regular time) per}$$
$$\text{machine-period of overtime production}$$

If we assume that management wishes to formulate a policy which will minimize expected costs, the criterion function may be written as

$$C(M) = C_1 M + C_2 \int_M^\infty (m - M) f(m) \, dm$$

where $C(M)$ is the expected cost of a policy of providing M machines.

With the aid of the theorem given below we compute the optimal policy by setting

$$\frac{dC(M)}{dM} = 0$$

Theorem: Let

$$g(y) = \int_{u_0(y)}^{u_1(y)} f(x,y) \, dx$$

then

$$\frac{dg(y)}{dy} = \int_{u_0(y)}^{u_1(y)} \frac{\partial f(x,y)}{\partial y} \, dx - f(u_0, y) \frac{du_0}{dy} + f(u_1, y) \frac{du_1}{dy}$$

We let

$$y = M \qquad\qquad u_0 = M$$
$$x = m \qquad\qquad u_1 = \overline{m} = \text{maximum value of } m$$
$$f(x,y) = (m - M)f(m)$$

Then

$$\frac{\partial f(x,y)}{\partial y} = -f(m) \qquad f(u_0, y) = (M - M)f(M) = 0$$
$$\frac{du_0}{dy} = 1 \qquad\qquad f(u_1, y) = (\overline{m} - M)f(\overline{m})$$
$$\frac{du_1}{dy} = 0$$

Using these results as indicated by the theorem, it follows that

$$\frac{dC(m)}{dM} = C_1 + C_2 \int\limits_{M}^{\overline{m}} - f(m)dm - (0)(1) + (\overline{m} - M)f(\overline{m})(0)$$

Finally we set this derivative equal to zero and let the value of M which satisfies the resulting equation be M^*. The result turns out to be the value of m, say M^*, which satisfies the following relation.

$$\int\limits_{0}^{M^*} f(m)dm = F(M^*) = \frac{C_2 - C_1}{C_2}$$

(We have assumed that M is a continuous variable, but this is easily corrected.)

Whether this model actually fits the real decision to a useful extent depends on a number of crucial assumptions, some of which have been mentioned previously. In addition we have assumed a linear cost structure, and implicitly a number of assumptions would be involved in the computation of the effectiveness factor. Fitting the model is, of course, a tremendous tactical problem.

Strategic Considerations

Let us assume that the tactical problem of the model could be dealt with and examine some of the strategic questions suggested earlier. Clearly the risk approach requires a large amount of data that may be difficult, if not impossible, to obtain in an actual situation. For example, it may not be possible to obtain performance time distributions for operations in the planning stage. If similar operations are already under way, the data may be available. If not, however, the only recourse may be to a synthetic time system which will roughly give the mean performance time.[6] There may easily be such a large degree of uncertainty connected with the future production program that no forecast can be made. One must also recognize those situations in which the data could be obtained but limitations of time and expense prevent it. It must be emphasized, however, that even if the data are not completely available, the model itself may be of real value, as we will indicate.

The model itself presents a number of difficulties which we have outlined, but these may be overcome by anyone familiar with probability theory and the calculus. Actually there are some hidden difficulties of model construction underlying the effectiveness factor which has been used. Suppose, for example, that we have an operation that is under statistical control with respect to a particular quality attribute, and its mean

---

[6]For a comprehensive explanation of performance time determination, see Gerald Nadler, *Work Systems Design: The Ideals Concept* (Irwin Series in Operations Management [Homewood, Ill.: Richard D. Irwin, Inc., 1967]), chap. 9.

scrap rate is p. One wants to know how many pieces to make in order to get, say, D good pieces. Here again one may resort to averages and say that the average number of pieces to be made to yield D good ones is given by

$$\frac{D}{1-p}$$

Alternatively, one might wish to be more accurate and say that the probability of having to produce $D + k$ pieces in order to obtain D good pieces is given by

$$\phi(D, k, p) = \frac{(D + k - 1)!}{k!(D - 1)!}p^k(1 - p)^D$$

This is obtained by noting that the probability of having to produce $D + k$ pieces in order to obtain D good pieces is the product of the probability of k defectives in $D + k - 1$ pieces times the probability that the last piece produced (piece number $D + k$) will be good.

Probability of k defectives in $D + k - 1$ pieces =

$$\frac{(D + k - 1)!}{k!(D - 1)!}p^k(1 - p)^{D-1}$$

Probability that the last piece is good $= 1 - p$

FIGURE 5–2

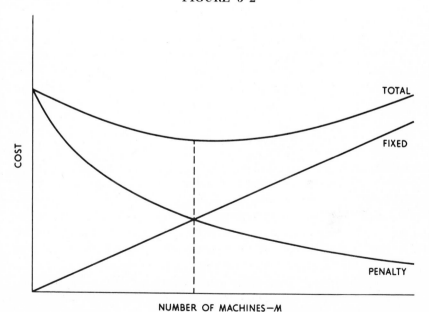

NUMBER OF MACHINES—M

Thus, the model itself may become quite complicated. Experience seems to indicate that it is worthwhile introducing probability distributions as we have done, but that very complicated distributions may perhaps go too far. The step from assumed certainty to risk is nearly always warranted even if the data are not fully available. This step introduces the entire notion of establishing a fixed number of machines in the department, against a requirement which is actually subject to variation. Many feel

FIGURE 5-3

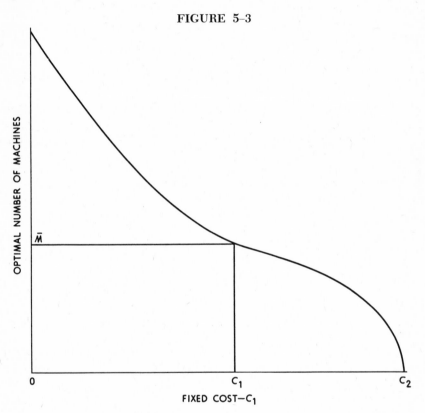

that if the analyst makes explicit for management the sort of cost function just given, this is itself of considerable value as a basis for management decisions.

The final strategic consideration which was suggested was that of the acceptance by management. This depends heavily on personalities and local factors of course, but something can be said about the benefits of recognizing risk. Let us suppose that the variables in our model are in fact subject to variation, as they are in many situations. The important question then is "How costly will be the errors in our plans if we base them on the assumed certainty approach?"

Figure 5–2 shows the form of a typical cost function and indicates the property of the optimal number of machines. That is, if we plan for any other number of machines, total expected cost will increase. Figure 5–3 indicates the relation between the costs and the optimal number of machines. As C_1 becomes small relative to C_2 more and more machines should be planned for, and contrariwise. If we neglect these costs completely and select a number of machines equal to the average requirement, this is equivalent to assuming values for C_1 and C_2. To the extent that these values are in error, the number of machines will be in error, and thus the cost will be increased.

Figure 5–4 indicates the result of failing to recognize the variation in the required number of machines. As the variation increases, the optimal number of machines increases, and thus the error made by planning for the average machine requirement also increases, if

$$\frac{C_2 - C_1}{C_2} > F(\overline{M})$$

Finally, Figure 5–5 indicates the difference in total expected costs for the two methods as a function of the variation. Clearly, the more variation present in the machine requirement, the more costly it becomes to overlook variation and plan by using average values.

FIGURE 5–4

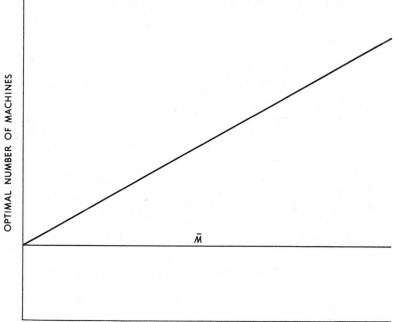

STANDARD DEVIATION OF m

The Discrete Case

The model may be modified to reflect the fact that the number of machines installed is a discrete, rather than a continuous variable. In this case we would seek to minimize the function

$$C(M) = C_1 M + C_2 \sum_{m=M}^{\infty} (m - M)f(m)$$

FIGURE 5-5

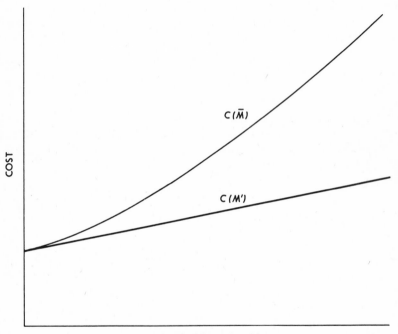

COST

STANDARD DEVIATION OF *m*

The optimal value of M will satisfy the pair of inequalities

$$C(M^* + 1) - C(M^*) \geqslant 0$$
$$C(M^* - 1) - C(M^*) \geqslant 0$$

These expressions can be reduced to the double inequality below

$$F(M^* - 1) \leqslant \frac{C_2 - C_1}{C_2} \leqslant F(M^*)$$

Planning Horizon

This model may be interpreted in two ways so far as the implications it holds for the capacity planning horizon. Suppose the firm considers changes in capacity at the beginning of certain time periods only, say once a year. Because of the lags in bringing new capacity into operation, the firm decides what its capacity will be at the start of a period, and will not alter that capacity until the start of a subsequent period. Now if the demand distributions are predicted to be the same for each period in the indefinite future, then the capacity should presumably be the same and the model serves to indicate what this capacity might be. If however, the demand distribution is predicted to change from period to period, what capacity the firm elects for one period is presumably influenced by the demand distributions for subsequent periods. For this case, the model can be interpreted as having a planning horizon of only one period. In other words, it suggests a capacity for the current period without regard to the position it will place the firm in with respect to future periods with different demands. The interesting question for the systems designer is whether the benefits from enriching the model would outweigh the costs of doing so, in view of the uncertainty of future demand forecasts and the futurity of future cash flows.

PROBLEMS

1. Assume the probability distribution of m is a uniform distribution over the range $90 < m \leqslant 110$.

   a) If $C_1 = \$20$ and $C_2 = \$25$, find the number of machines which will minimize total expected cost.

   b) Find the number of machines which will fix the probability of working overtime at .10.

   c) Find the number of machines which will make the probability of any machines being idle during regular production time equal to .05.

2. Consider a plant in which $f(m)$ is normally distributed with a mean of 100 machines. For values of the standard deviation of m equal to 10, 20, and 30 machines, and for values of

$$\frac{C_2 - C_1}{C_2}$$

equal to .50, .60, .80, and .90, find the number of machines which minimizes expected cost.

SUGGESTIONS FOR FURTHER STUDY

HINOMOTO, HIROHIDE. "Capacity Expansion with Facilities under Technological Improvement," *Management Science*, Vol. 11, No. 5 (March, 1965).

HOLT, CHARLES C.; MODIGLIANI, FRANCO; MUTH, JOHN F.; and SIMON, HERBERT A. *Planning Production, Inventories, and Work Force.* Englewood Cliffs, N.J.: Prentice-Hall, Inc., 1960.

MEYER, JOHN R., and KUH, EDWIN. *The Investment Decision—An Empirical Study.* Cambridge, Mass.: Harvard University Press, 1957.

NORD, OLE C. *Growth of a New Product—Effects of Capacity Acquisition Policies.* Cambridge, Mass.: The Massachusetts Institute of Technology Press, 1963.

Chapter 6

CAPITAL BUDGETING SYSTEMS

Management Systems

As a FIRM grows it becomes increasingly important to have an effective management system for delegating and controlling capital investment decisions. The administrative arrangements by which the logic of the previous chapters is applied are at least as important as the details of the logic itself. In many firms management systems for capital budgeting have gradually evolved and the systems designer may find great difficulty in overcoming the organizational inertia which opposes changes in them. Yet some analysis of these systems may suggest the direction in which such evolution should be directed, when opportunities to do so appear.

There are five basic functions to be performed by a management system for capital budgeting. The system must *search* out opportunities for capital investment or generate proposals for programs involving capital outlays.[1] These proposals must be *evaluated* in the sense of obtaining the data on cash flows and their uncertainty which will permit a decision to be made. The system must *communicate* to those who make the decision both the proposals and their supporting data as well as predictions of the availability of capital. A *budgeting decision* must be made which allocates funds to proposals in such a manner as to best implement the long- and intermediate-range plans for optimal capital *structure*.[2] Fi-

---

[1]Professor Herbert A. Simon's "intelligence function." For an explanation of the role of this "step" in decision making, see H. L. Timms, *Introduction to Operations Management* (Irwin Series in Operations Management [Homewood, Ill.: Richard D. Irwin, Inc., 1967]), chap. 3.

[2]An example of integrated decision systems. For an explanation of the integration of financial plans, including capital structure, and capacity planning, see H. L. Timms, *Introduction to Operations Management* (Irwin Series in Operations Management [Homewood, Ill.: Richard D. Irwin, Inc., 1967]), chap. 5.

nally, the system must provide for *control* of the way in which the funded proposals are implemented and a comparison of their actual results with those predicted at the time of the decision. The problem of designing an effective management system involves finding an arrangement or delegation of these functions to organizational units or divisions, achieving good communication among the units, and providing for coordination of the resulting decisions. Before looking at this somewhat complex system design problem, it may be useful to consider the basic functions in greater detail.

Search

Some capital investment opportunities are literally forced upon a firm. Little search effort and little choice are involved as in the case of the failure of a major component of the production system. An investment obviously must be made. Beyond these are the opportunities which permit the firm greater discretion. Some firms generate an ample supply of investment proposals in the normal course of business affairs, and thus the amount of effort devoted to search is not a matter of deliberate policy. In others, an important element of system design is the regulation of the flow of proposals to properly match the flow of capital funds available for investment. The operating divisions generate proposals for equipment replacement, for new processes, and for cost reduction. From product development and long-range planning groups come opportunities to expand capacity in current lines and to move into new ones. Top management may develop plans for major acquisitions leading to integration or diversification.

Search, especially in the sense of research, is a highly uncertain undertaking and must often be justified on the vaguest of grounds. When a firm adopts a policy of spending say, a fixed percentage of sales on research each year, it is a little difficult to tell what the appropriate percentage should be. It is often impossible to say what investment opportunities will arise from research, when they will be available for commercial development, and whether capital will be in hand at the time. Yet a policy which relates research effort to sales may have a reasonable basis. As sales grow, for example, so retained earnings may grow and thus capital available for investment. Growing sales should thus be accompanied by growing research efforts so as to provide opportunities for investing these increasing funds. Likewise, growing sales in a particular product may, however crudely, be the signal that the market life of the product is now at such a point that it is time to undertake the research and development which will produce candidates to replace it as it fades.

There is little point in carrying on an extensive program to generate proposals if the funds available for investment are severely limited. On the other hand if funds are available, it is important that a level of search effort be mounted consistent with making good use of these funds. The determination of which organizational units are to carry on search and at what levels is thus basic to the design of a capital budgeting management system.

Evaluation

The discovery or emergence of an investment proposal brings with it various amounts of supporting information. Typically, however, a deliberate decision is made as to whether the proposal is sufficiently well understood as to warrant no further efforts toward uncertainty reduction, or whether additional evaluation is required prior to the decision step. Evaluation, once undertaken, may be a sequential process in which it is repeatedly asked, "Is enough now known about the proposal to make a decision, or is there still too much uncertainty?"

The need for evaluation arises essentially out of the subjective uncertainty that a decision maker associates with a proposal. This uncertainty is seldom precisely defined and often entirely implicit. Thus it is most difficult for the decision maker to effectively communicate his uncertainty to those doing the evaluation. Likewise many proposals involve as part of their supporting data, the judgments of technical experts or those with special knowledge and experience. Perhaps the most valuable aspect of these skilled judgmnts is this uncertainty felt by the person making them, yet again, this is most difficult to communicate. Some capital budgeting systems require proposals to contain only single-valued estimates, making no attempt at all to indicate uncertainty.

The problem of management systems design, as regards evaluation, is one both of communication and of coordination. There is little point in expending extensive effort to support a proposal which is already within the experience of management and thus not particularly uncertain. Nor is it worthwhile to evaluate a proposal which has little chance for funding in view of the availability of other clearly better ones which would more than exhaust the firm's capital funds.

If the task of evaluating a proposal is delegated to a division or subunit of the firm, the evaluation may well be biased in favor of what the division sees as its own interests. Thus the divisions of a firm, which must compete with each other for the available capital funds, quite naturally may produce optimistic evaluations of the propsals which they generate. The management system may thus include an independent check on the evaluation produced by the division as well as a feedback loop for determining to what extent funded proposals actually live up to their evaluation. Such a feedback hopefully has the effect of removing some of the bias from proposals, although the time lag involved in capital investments tends to weaken this effect.

Communication

If proposals must be transmitted from one organizational unit to another, say from an operating division to the board of directors, then the management system must provide an effective means for the transmission. The means typically vary from standard forms to personal appearances by those originating the proposal. It is particularly difficult to design a standardized format for reporting proposals, although this has obvious advantages in assuring uniformity and completeness of evaluation efforts. The basic difficulty is, as has been suggested, that of transmitting the uncertainty associated with the proposal. A system which requires single-valued estimates completely suppresses the uncertainty which may arise from the variability of the basic data, from the experience of those having original knowledge of the proposal, or from the judgments of specialized experts. In Chapter 2 the possibility of expressing these uncertainties using the framework of probability theory was outlined. This is not a "natural" language for expressing uncertainty and the central difficulty involved in using it is the need for it to be learned by those involved. It is no trivial problem to elicit from an experienced manager an expression of his uncertainty which can be captured in terms of probabilities. Yet it appears the best possibility currently available to the system designer.

It is obviously costly to put a proposal in a form for effective communication. This cost involves not only the direct effort, but the time delay and the inevitable loss of information which results. These considerations impel the systems designer to put the point of decision as close to the point of proposal origin as possible. Unfortunately, there are other effects which complicate this sort of solution to the communication problem.

Budget Dynamics

An organizational unit with a given amount of money[3] for a budget period may fund proposals in two basic ways. The proposals may be accumulated until the end of the period at which time the best are selected for funding. This opportunity to be selective increases the investment results achieved by the unit. If, for example, it could only choose to fund five proposals, then on the average the best 5 out of 100 proposals would be better than the best 5 out of 10. This policy, called batch budgeting, has the disadvantage of postponing implementation of the projects selected until the end of the budget period. While this will not be serious with large projects having a long gestation period, on others the delay may be a significant consideration.

---

[3]Determined in the financial planning process. See H. L. Timms, *Introduction to Operations Management* (Irwin Series in Operations Management [Homewood, Ill.: Richard D. Irwin, Inc., 1967]), chap. 5.

If a unit expects fewer proposals during a budget period than it has funds to undertake, then there is no real motive to accumulate them for batch budgeting. Indeed, a policy of continuous budgeting may be used, funding projects as they arise. Of course, the projects funded must meet some criteria for acceptability in order to be included in a continuous budgeting plan. If the unit anticipates more projects than it can fund during a period, it may still wish to use continuous budgeting in order to reduce the delays in implementing projects. Here the problem is to choose a level of acceptability, perhaps expressed in terms of an interest rate, so that the best proposals are funded. It would be desirable to avoid using available funds early in the period, only to have better proposals emerge later. The general design problem is thus to choose a level of acceptability which keeps those projects funded on a continuous basis as good as possible, without sacrificing the advantage of a quick response.

Control

An effective management system for capital budgeting will perhaps include two kinds of control. When a project is authorized, controls will be required on the progress of its implementation. These controls keep management aware of the development of the project in order to reveal troubles in time for appropriate corrective action.[4] They also permit plans to be made as to the cash requirements of the firm, both the consumption of cash as new projects go forward and the renewed inflow as they begin to earn. These controls signal to management those projects which are likely to overrun their proposed budgets. Typically the uncertainties of cost estimating are recognized by permitting overruns of some modest size to be funded without further consideration. Larger overruns may require special budget requests, however.

The second type of control is the post-completion audit of a project. This study attempts to verify the savings or profits estimated in the proposal, and to reveal the reasons for failure. It is an important basis for estimating the bias and reliability of future proposals, and may be used to avoid the introduction of deliberate bias in the proposals submitted by the divisions of the firm. A division manager who knows his projects will be postaudited may be motivated to use considerably more care in estimating their profitability. The postaudit is often a very difficult step. Sometimes the conditions which prevailed at the time of decision are greatly changed at the time of implementation, sometimes it is impossible to identify the savings or profits associated with a particular investment, and sometimes the records of the firm are simply inade-

---

[4]Increasingly popular methods of planning and subsequent control of the progress of a project are the techniques called PERT and PERT/Cost. These are explained in James H. Greene, *Operations Planning and Control* (Irwin Series in Operations Management [Homewood, Ill.: Richard D. Irwin, Inc., 1967]), chap. 5.

quate for the task. Since many of the purposes of the postaudit can be accomplished nearly as well by auditing a sample of projects rather than all of them, a basic design problem is that of how this sample is to be selected.

Design Problems

The problems of designing a management system which will produce effective performance of these basic functions are clearly difficult, and no ready-made prescriptions are available. In the remainder of this chapter an attempt is made to draw out the basic issues and illustrate them by means of an example which is characteristic of current management systems in industry. The problem of system design might be put, "How can these functions be assigned to various organizational units and how can coordination among these units be provided, so as to produce effective investment results?" This may be thought of in terms, for example, of the large multidivisional firm which consists of a corporate management or headquarters group and a number of operating divisions. Which of these functions should be performed by the headquarters group, and which delegated to the operating divisions? How is coordination to be assured between the functions performed by headquarters, and those performed by the divisions? How can coordination among the divisions themselves be effectively arranged? Viewed this way, the design problem has two basic aspects. First, how can functions be delegated so as to best take advantage of the complementaries or economies arising from having a group of functions performed by a given organizational unit? Second, with the functions delegated to various units, how can their performance be coordinated so as to serve the objectives of the firm as a whole?

Complementarities

The advantages of various delegation arrangements in capital budgeting systems may be suggested with a few examples. Suppose one considers a fully centralized budgeting system in which all proposals are sent to the headquarters group, which retains sole discretion as to which will be funded. This may be compared with a decentralized system in which each of the operating divisions is given a budget and permitted to fund whichever of its proposals it wishes. The obvious advantage of the centralized plan is that headquarters has a wider horizon of choice than any division. That is, it may choose the best of all the proposals generated by the firm, rather than select from those generated by a single division. Thus one would expect the headquarters group to be able to invest the firm's funds more effectively. The interesting design question is whether headquarters, which has not only more proposals but more funds under centralization, can actually in the long run be more selective than the divisions acting individually under decentralization.

Similarly, by centralizing the control of funds, the firm does not find itself in the situation of one operating division having some excellent proposals, but inadequate funds, while another division has only fair proposals and ample funds. Centralization also permits the headquarters group to bring the experience of the entire company to bear on a given plan and to justify the employment of specialists of all sorts to aid in the evaluation of a plan. On the other hand, some complementarities suggest decentralization. There are advantages both in reduced delays and in the presence of special knowledge and skills which suggest the decision can best be made by the operating division which originates the proposal. A division permitted to make its own investment decisions and held accountable for the results may well be motivated toward better evaluation of its proposals than would otherwise be the case.

Coordination

As soon, however, as some of these functions are delegated, problems of coordination arise. The level of search effort carried on by the operating divisions must be coordinated with the funds available to the firm. The amount of evaluation effort devoted to a proposal must likewise be coordinated with the number of proposals being generated and the funds which the firm wishes to invest. There is little point in one division devoting considerable effort to the development of a proposal when another division has already produced a clearly good one which will use up the available funds. Similarly, divisions acting independently may develop similar or competing proposals duplicating or negating each other's efforts.

Centralized Systems

Historically capital budgeting systems in industry have been more centralized than decentralized. An analysis of these systems suggests the following hypotheses which may be useful to the systems designer.

1. Central control of funds is one of the basic sources of strength for a large firm. The basic principle of organization for many firms is to centralize the major policy and long-range planning functions, while delegating the day-to-day operating problems. Centralized decision making on long-term investments is the major source of the headquarters group's power to influence the destiny of the firm. It can choose among a large and diversified group of proposals, seeking a program which is best from a company, rather than a divisional, point of view.

2. As we have suggested already, this central control raises the need for communication of proposals from the divisions to headquarters and for some headquarters' control over the statements and actions of the divisions.

3. Central control over capital budgeting solves directly the problem of coordinating the investment plans of the divisions among themselves and coordinating these plans with the availability of funds for the firm.

4. The firm may elect central control of capital budgeting as a primary means of finding out and controlling what is going on in the divisions. That is, it may be centralized less out of intrinsic necessity, than out of a choice of capital budgeting as a primary means of organizational control. Certainly long-range planning, if it exists in a firm, is likely to be highly centralized, and capital budgeting control may be the basic means of implementing the strategic, long-range plans.

5. On the other side of the coin, factors which impel the firm toward some degree of decentralization in capital budgeting were clear very early as well. These include:

a) The need to avoid using up the energies of the headquarters group on a large number of small capital proposals.

b) The "rubber stamp" effect. The uselessness of submitting to headquarters certain proposals which are generally agreed to be essential and well justified. If headquarters routinely approves such proposals they might well be handled at the operating levels.

c) The presence of information and judgments at the operating level which cannot be effectively communicated to the higher levels. For example, it is traditional to suppress most of the uncertainty associated with an investment proposal when it is written up for transmission. Indeed, there is seldom a conventional, effective means of expressing this uncertainty. Now the headquarters group must either supply its own judgments of uncertainty or neglect those uncertainty considerations which were evident at the operating levels. This tends to place a premium on using decision makers at headquarters that have some familiarity with divisional problems.

d) Decentralizing the capital budgeting process may be closely associated with the incentive aspects of decentralization in general. Thus when a division manager is instructed to take the responsibility for his division in a manner approaching the responsibility of an entrepreneur, capital budgeting should be included to some extent. If his rewards are related to his achievements, then presumably his responsibility and authority must include a significant range of investment decisions.

e) The time required for a proposal to reach headquarters and for a decision to be returned may be substantial. Thus the need to give the firm a quicker reaction time (or shorter gestation period on proposals) impels one toward some degree of decentralization.

6. Finally, out of these conflicting considerations, it is not surprising that organizations should emerge which are neither highly centralized nor highly decentralized. The better organizational designs seem to lie somewhere between the two extremes.[5] When such a need for "mixed" system exists, one may well expect to find that the evolutionary process by which the organization seeks a workable design is an attended one. Of greater extent perhaps than would be the case if the optimum lay in one of the purer forms of organization, either highly centralized or highly decentralized.

Patterns of Delegation

The effectiveness of a mixed system may be sought through several basic delegation plans.

1. Proposals which are clearly "good" in terms of rate of return or present worth per dollar invested might be delegated to the operating divisions. A clearly good project is, by definition, one which would be funded if sent up to headquarters. Thus nothing is gained by doing so, provided appropriate controls can be maintained over the total amount invested by the divisions in this way and over the bias and reliability of divisional proposal estimates.

2. Certain classes of proposals could be funded at the discretion of the divisions, such as routine replacement proposals. Investments in new processes or new product facilities would require the approval of headquarters. Projects about which there is little uncertainty, which can be evaluated by routinized methods, and which represent execution of policies already established by headquarters, are thus funded by the divisions. Again, the need for controls is obvious.

3. Perhaps commonest in actual management systems is the principle that large projects must go up to headquarters, while small projects may be handled by the divisions themselves. This is often coupled with a budget limitation establishing the maximum total investment in small projects which a division may undertake in a budget period.

The prevalence of this third pattern of delegation in actual organizations suggests that it might be useful to explore in some detail the design problems which it presents. Since the critical separation of projects for decision at divisional or headquarters level is based on the size of

---

[5]For an explanation of a compromise between the two extremes wherein budgeting is accomplished simultaneously "from the bottom" (decentralized) up, and the top (centralized) down," with the resulting differences resolved through incremental analysis, see H. L. Timms, *Introduction to Operations Management* (Irwin Series in Management [Homewood, Ill.: Richard D. Irwin, Inc., 1967]), chap. 5.

initial investment required, these systems have been called size gate systems. The initial investment which distinguishes a large from a small project is called the gate value. Where a divisional budget restriction is imposed on the volume of small projects funded, the name "size gate and division budget system" is used.

Size Gate Policies and Objectives

In one large firm proposals calling for an initial investment of less than $25,000 can be made at the discretion of a division manager, while larger ones must go up to the corporate headquarters for final decision. Indeed, in some firms there are several such levels of delegation, specifying various project sizes which may be funded at various levels in the organization. Such systems lead immediately to the question of why the gate value of $25,000 was chosen, why the size of the initial investment is an effective basis for defining the degree of decentralization, and what would happen if the gate value were changed?

The motivations for such management systems include:

a) Regulating the workloads at both levels of the organization, leaving the divisions free to deal with operating problems and the headquarters group free to deal with long-range policy.

b) Maintaining control over the major directions of investment at headquarters.

c) Permitting headquarters to take advantage of the complementarities arising from a wider horizon of choice.

d) Allowing the divisions to carry out small investments which do not greatly influence the overall direction of company investment.

e) Implementing without delay the small projects which would usually be approved by headquarters anyway, but only after making their way through the process of referral up to the corporate level and back.

f) Attempting roughly at least to get the decisions made at the levels at which the best judgment, experience, and information are available.

The two basic design questions concern the gate value to be used and the proportion of the firm's funds to be allocated to each division for investment in small projects. We consider first the choice of gate value.

Different classes of projects, such as replacement, cost reduction, or expansion and new product proposals may be handled by different methods in the firm. For example, as standardized methods of analyzing particular classes of investments are developed, the gate values for these classes may be increased. This is, in part, a reflection of the fact that standardized methods of investment analysis tend to standardize the level of uncertainty associated with a class of projects by fixing the amount of information obtained. If the headquarters group can effectively communicate to the divisions the decision processes it would use in such standardized situations, the divisions become increasingly capable of reproducing the headquarters' choices, and thus the gate value may be increased with little change in the resulting investment action. In other words, as the probability of headquarters' confirming a divisional decision increases, the gate value tends to be increased. It is most important to note the difference between divisional ability to reproduce headquarters' decisions and divisional motivation to do so.

The basic question is, clearly, what will happen to the investment results achieved by the firm as the gate value is changed?

The size of the divisional budget restriction is likely to depend for its effectiveness, at least partly, on its relation to the gate value of the firm. High gate values with low division budgets and low gate values with high division budgets would appear to negate many of the advantages outlined for these systems. The problem, of course, is to get some estimate of the effectiveness, say in terms of the firm's investment results, of various combinations of gate value and division budget.

Other design problems for size gate and division budget systems include the degree to which the management of search effort is to be delegated. If the generation of large and small projects cannot be independently controlled, then a single policy on search effort produces some mix of project sizes. In such a case, some coordination would seem to be required in order to effectively match search, gate value, and divisional budget allocation. Similarly the amount of evaluation effort may be dictated by headquarters, left to the divisions, or taken to depend on the nature of the project. For example, the divisions may be permitted to evaluate small projects as they wish, while large projects are evaluated according to headquarters directives.

While general answers are not available to these kinds of design problems, some hypotheses might be provided which would suggest to the analyst the sort of questions which might be fruitfully studied.

Example

Consider a firm with several divisions which is to be operated on a size gate and division budget basis. The divisions are each of about the same size, in the sense that they each produce about the same number of investment proposals in an average budget period. The generation of large and small projects cannot be controlled independently. A common gate value is to apply to all divisions, and funds allocated to the divisions are to be divided equally among them. The levels of search effort at the divisions are such that for any of the designs to be considered, both the divisions and the headquarters group will have ample projects from which to choose. Under this assumption, both would perhaps use batch budgeting in order to be selective. Yet, because of the delay effects the divisions might wish to use continuous budgeting. All of the projects generated in the firm came from the divisions, the headquarters group carrying on no search. Suppose the designer could alter the gate value, the division budget allocation, and the amount of search effort.

Some Design Problems

Among the first questions a designer would face in this situation might be the effects of these system characteristics on the investment results achieved by the firm. For example:

1. If the gate value is increased, what would happen to the investment results achieved by the headquarters group? One might expect headquarters' results to decline since they would have to invest the same amount of money in projects selected from among a decreasing number of proposals.

2. If the divisions are using batch budgeting, what would happen to their investment results as the gate value is increased? Since the divisions would have a larger amount of proposals from which to select the projects they will fund, divisional investment results might be expected to increase.

3. What would happen to the investment results for the firm as a whole if the gate value is increased? If headquarters' and divisional budgets are held constant, and if batch budgeting is used throughout, then the firm's investment results might first increase and then decrease. Indeed, there might be an optimal gate value under these conditions. It might further be the case that the optimal gate value is one which makes the ratio of the number of projects funded to the number of proposals considered approximately equal for each organizational unit.

4. How sensitive would the system's investment results be to changes in the gate value? If the number of proposals generated by the firm is large relative to the funds available for investment, the system's investment results might be relatively sensitive to changes in gate value as long as the budget allocations were kept in the sort of relationship suggested above. If this turns out to be the case, then it suggests the means for achieving many of the advantages of partial decentralization without significant sacrifices in investment results.

5. The same question may be asked somewhat differently: If the gate value is fixed, what would happen to investment results as budget allocations are changed? As before one might hypothesize that the optimal budget allocation is one which makes the ratio of projects funded to proposals considered approximately equal for each organizational unit. Further, the greater the number of proposals considered by the firm relative to the funds available, the less sensitive one might expect investment results would be to changes in budget allocations as long as each unit funds roughly the same proportion of proposals.

6. What happens to the firm's investment results if both gate value and division budget allocations are increased? That is, what happens as the degree of decentralization is increased? One would expect that, even if gate values and budget allocations are kept in the most desirable relationship, the firm's investment results would decline as the degree of decentralization is increased. A decentralized system is unlikely to be better than a fully centralized one so far as investment results are concerned. If this is the case, then these advantages of decentralization must lie elsewhere.

7. If the divisions use a policy of continuous budgeting in order to reduce the delay in implementing their "small" projects, what would happen to system results as the degree of decentralization is increased? The problem of the optimal relation between gate value and division budget allocation is most difficult in this case, yet one would generally expect as before, that the system would not do as well if partially decentralized as it would if fully centralized. Divisions investing without being selective would make poorer use of funds than headquarters' investment on a selective basis.

Delegation of Search Policy

If we continue the assumption that the generation of large and small projects cannot be controlled independently, then we may be concerned with what would happen if divisions are permitted to control search efforts. Divisions may adopt a policy of discontinuing search when they have, under continuous budgeting, exhausted their budget allocations. This policy offers no assurance of producing an appropriate number of proposals for headquarters' consideration.

Suppose, for example, divisions decide to choose in advance of a budget period a level of search effort which will, in the face of a given division budget and gate value, assure ample projects with some probability. If the marginal cost of increasing search effort above this level is less than the marginal increase in headquarters' investment results at this level of search effort, then the firm would gain by a higher level of search effort. Since the divisions do not consider the marginal gain at headquarters, they will not generally select an optimal level of search effort.

Several alternatives to the complete delegation of search decisions may be noted.

1. Full centralization may be used in which headquarters establishes search policy based on a fixed gate size, an optimal allocation of funds based on gate size and level of search, and the marginal gain to the firm from increases in search effort.

2. Divisions may choose levels of search effort based not only on their own budgets, but on their "share" of headquarters' investment results. This requires that each division know the headquarters' budget and

the distribution of the number of projects submitted to headquarters by all other divisions.

3. Headquarters may "pay" a division for the proposals it submits, regulating the price to bring the divisions to adopt a level of search effort which is optimal for the firm.

4. Headquarters may note that the level of search effort elected by the divisions is a function of the division budget allocations. Headquarters may thus attempt to use budget allocations to control not only the volume of divisional investment but also the amount of search which they choose. If we suppose, for example, that the level of search effort elected by the divisions is proportional to their budget allocations, then the effectiveness of the system depends on the magnitude of the constant of proportionality.

These remarks are, of course, only hypotheses. There is little evidence as to the effects of gate value, division budget, or levels of search in particular firms. They are intended only to suggest the sort of questions which need to be investigated if one is to consider modifications in a capital budgeting system. They represent an attempt to say something specific about a systems problem rather than take refuge in vague generalities. The questions suggested deal only with the operational or economic measures of systems performance. One must also be concerned with a whole range of questions about the motivational effects of partial decentralization on the performance of division managers, the benefits of relieving top management of responsibility for day-to-day operations, the importance of delays in implementing proposals, and so on. Characteristically, the system designer begins with the more measurable aspects of his system, and realizes that he cannot bring all of it within the purview of his analysis. This, however, does not prevent him from making a substantial contribution to the design and evolution of an effective management decision system.

•

INTEREST TABLES*

½ Percent Interest

n	Given P To find S $(1 + i)^n$	Given S To find P $\dfrac{1}{(1 + i)^n}$	Given R To find S $\dfrac{(1 + i)^n - 1}{i}$	Given S To find R $\dfrac{i}{(1 + i)^n - 1}$	Given R To find P $\dfrac{(1 + i)^n - 1}{i(1 + i)^n}$	Given P To find R $\dfrac{i(1 + i)^n}{(1 + i)^n - 1}$	n
1	1.005	0.9950	1.000	1.00000	0.995	1.00500	1
2	1.010	0.9901	2.005	0.49875	1.985	0.50375	2
3	1.015	0.9851	3.015	0.33167	2.970	0.33667	3
4	1.020	0.9802	4.030	0.24813	3.950	0.25313	4
5	1.025	0.9754	5.050	0.19801	4.926	0.20301	5
6	1.030	0.9705	6.076	0.16460	5.896	0.16960	6
7	1.036	0.9657	7.106	0.14073	6.862	0.14573	7
8	1.041	0.9609	8.141	0.12283	7.823	0.12783	8
9	1.046	0.9561	9.182	0.10891	8.779	0.11391	9
10	1.051	0.9513	10.228	0.09777	9.730	0.10277	10
11	1.056	0.9466	11.279	0.08866	10.677	0.09366	11
12	1.062	0.9419	12.336	0.08107	11.619	0.08607	12
13	1.067	0.9372	13.397	0.07464	12.556	0.07964	13
14	1.072	0.9326	14.464	0.06914	13.489	0.07414	14
15	1.078	0.9279	15.537	0.06436	14.417	0.06936	15
16	1.083	0.9233	16.614	0.06019	15.340	0.06519	16
17	1.088	0.9187	17.697	0.05651	16.259	0.06151	17
18	1.094	0.9141	18.786	0.05323	17.173	0.05823	18
19	1.099	0.9096	19.880	0.05030	18.082	0.05530	19
20	1.105	0.9051	20.979	0.04767	18.987	0.05267	20
21	1.110	0.9006	22.084	0.04528	19.888	0.05028	21
22	1.116	0.8961	23.194	0.04311	20.784	0.04811	22
23	1.122	0.8916	24.310	0.04113	21.676	0.04613	23
24	1.127	0.8872	25.432	0.03932	22.563	0.04432	24
25	1.133	0.8828	26.559	0.03765	23.446	0.04265	25
26	1.138	0.8784	27.692	0.03611	24.324	0.04111	26
27	1.144	0.8740	28.830	0.03469	25.198	0.03969	27
28	1.150	0.8697	29.975	0.03336	26.068	0.03836	28
29	1.156	0.8653	31.124	0.03213	26.933	0.03713	29
30	1.161	0.8610	32.280	0.03098	27.794	0.03598	30
31	1.167	0.8567	33.441	0.02990	28.651	0.03490	31
32	1.173	0.8525	34.609	0.02889	29.503	0.03389	32
33	1.179	0.8482	35.782	0.02795	30.352	0.03295	33
34	1.185	0.8440	36.961	0.02706	31.196	0.03206	34
35	1.191	0.8398	38.145	0.02622	32.035	0.03122	35
40	1.221	0.8191	44.159	0.02265	36.172	0.02765	40
45	1.252	0.7990	50.324	0.01987	40.207	0.02487	45
50	1.283	0.7793	56.645	0.01765	44.143	0.02265	50

---

*Adapted with permission from H. G. Thuesen, *Engineering Economy* (2d ed.; Englewood Cliffs, N.J.: Prentice-Hall, Inc., 1957).

The Capacity Decision System

n	Given P To find S $(1 + i)^n$	Given S To find P $\dfrac{1}{(1 + i)^n}$	Given R To find S $\dfrac{(1 + i)^n - 1}{i}$	Given S To find R $\dfrac{i}{(1 + i)^n - 1}$	Given R To find P $\dfrac{(1 + i)^n - 1}{i(1 + i)^n}$	Given P To find R $\dfrac{i(1 + i)^n}{(1 + i)^n - 1}$	n
1	1.010	0.9901	1.000	1.00000	0.990	1.01000	1
2	1.020	0.9803	2.010	0.49751	1.970	0.50751	2
3	1.030	0.9706	3.030	0.33002	2.941	0.34002	3
4	1.041	0.9610	4.060	0.24628	3.902	0.25628	4
5	1.051	0.9515	5.101	0.19604	4.853	0.20604	5
6	1.062	0.9420	6.152	0.16255	5.795	0.17255	6
7	1.072	0.9327	7.214	0.13863	6.728	0.14863	7
8	1.083	0.9235	8.286	0.12069	7.652	0.13069	8
9	1.094	0.9143	9.369	0.10674	8.566	0.11674	9
10	1.105	0.9053	10.462	0.09558	9.471	0.10558	10
11	1.116	0.8963	11.567	0.08645	10.368	0.09645	11
12	1.127	0.8874	12.683	0.07885	11.255	0.08885	12
13	1.138	0.8787	13.809	0.07241	12.134	0.08241	13
14	1.149	0.8700	14.947	0.06690	13.004	0.07690	14
15	1.161	0.8613	16.097	0.06212	13.865	0.07212	15
16	1.173	0.8528	17.258	0.05794	14.718	0.06794	16
17	1.184	0.8444	18.430	0.05426	15.562	0.06426	17
18	1.196	0.8360	19.615	0.05098	16.398	0.06098	18
19	1.208	0.8277	20.811	0.04805	17.226	0.05805	19
20	1.220	0.8195	22.019	0.04542	18.046	0.05542	20
21	1.232	0.8114	23.239	0.04303	18.857	0.05303	21
22	1.245	0.8034	24.472	0.04086	19.660	0.05086	22
23	1.257	0.7954	25.716	0.03889	20.456	0.04889	23
24	1.270	0.7876	26.973	0.03707	21.243	0.04707	24
25	1.282	0.7798	28.243	0.03541	22.023	0.04541	25
26	1.295	0.7720	29.526	0.03387	22.795	0.04387	26
27	1.308	0.7644	30.821	0.03245	23.560	0.04245	27
28	1.321	0.7568	32.129	0.03112	24.316	0.04112	28
29	1.335	0.7493	33.450	0.02990	25.066	0.03990	29
30	1.348	0.7419	34.785	0.02875	25.808	0.03875	30
31	1.361	0.7346	36.133	0.02768	26.542	0.03768	31
32	1.375	0.7273	37.494	0.02667	27.270	0.03667	32
33	1.389	0.7201	38.869	0.02573	27.990	0.03573	33
34	1.403	0.7130	40.258	0.02484	28.703	0.03484	34
35	1.417	0.7059	41.660	0.02400	29.409	0.03400	35
40	1.489	0.6717	48.886	0.02046	32.835	0.03046	40
45	1.565	0.6391	56.481	0.01771	36.095	0.02771	45
50	1.645	0.6080	64.463	0.01551	39.196	0.02551	50

1 Percent Interest

n	Given P To find S $(1 + i)^n$	Given S To find P $\dfrac{1}{(1 + i)^n}$	Given R To find S $\dfrac{(1 + i)^n - 1}{i}$	Given S To find R $\dfrac{i}{(1 + i)^n - 1}$	Given R To find P $\dfrac{(1 + i)^n - 1}{i(1 + i)^n}$	Given P To find R $\dfrac{i(1 + i)^n}{(1 + i)^n - 1}$	n
1	1.020	0.9804	1.000	1.00000	0.980	1.02000	1
2	1.040	0.9612	2.020	0.49505	1.942	0.51505	2
3	1.061	0.9423	3.060	0.32675	2.884	0.34675	3
4	1.082	0.9238	4.122	0.24262	3.808	0.26262	4
5	1.104	0.9057	5.204	0.19216	4.713	0.21216	5
6	1.126	0.8880	6.308	0.15853	5.601	0.17853	6
7	1.149	0.8706	7.434	0.13451	6.472	0.15451	7
8	1.172	0.8535	8.583	0.11651	7.325	0.13651	8
9	1.195	0.8368	9.755	0.10252	8.162	0.12252	9
10	1.219	0.8203	10.950	0.09133	8.983	0.11133	10
11	1.243	0.8043	12.169	0.08218	9.787	0.10218	11
12	1.268	0.7885	13.412	0.07456	10.575	0.09456	12
13	1.294	0.7730	14.680	0.06812	11.348	0.08812	13
14	1.319	0.7579	15.974	0.06260	12.106	0.08260	14
15	1.346	0.7430	17.293	0.05783	12.849	0.07783	15
16	1.373	0.7284	18.639	0.05365	13.578	0.07365	16
17	1.400	0.7142	20.012	0.04997	14.292	0.06997	17
18	1.428	0.7002	21.412	0.04670	14.992	0.06670	18
19	1.457	0.6864	22.841	0.04378	15.678	0.06378	19
20	1.486	0.6730	24.297	0.04116	16.351	0.06116	20
21	1.516	0.6598	25.783	0.03878	17.011	0.05878	21
22	1.546	0.6468	27.299	0.03663	17.658	0.05663	22
23	1.577	0.6342	28.845	0.03467	18.292	0.05467	23
24	1.608	0.6217	30.422	0.03287	18.914	0.05287	24
25	1.641	0.6095	32.030	0.03122	19.523	0.05122	25
26	1.673	0.5976	33.671	0.02970	20.121	0.04970	26
27	1.707	0.5859	35.344	0.02829	20.707	0.04829	27
28	1.741	0.5744	37.051	0.02699	21.281	0.04699	28
29	1.776	0.5631	38.792	0.02578	21.844	0.04578	29
30	1.811	0.5521	40.568	0.02465	22.396	0.04465	30
31	1.848	0.5412	42.379	0.02360	22.938	0.04360	31
32	1.885	0.5306	44.227	0.02261	23.468	0.04261	32
33	1.922	0.5202	46.112	0.02169	23.989	0.04169	33
34	1.961	0.5100	48.034	0.02082	24.499	0.04082	34
35	2.000	0.5000	49.994	0.02000	24.999	0.04000	35
40	2.208	0.4529	60.402	0.01656	27.355	0.03656	40
45	2.438	0.4102	71.893	0.01391	29.490	0.03391	45
50	2.692	0.3715	84.579	0.01182	31.424	0.03182	50

2 Percent Interest

The Capacity Decision System

n	Given P To find S $(1 + i)^n$	Given S To find P $\dfrac{1}{(1 + i)^n}$	Given R To find S $\dfrac{(1 + i)^n - 1}{i}$	Given S To find R $\dfrac{i}{(1 + i)^n - 1}$	Given R To find P $\dfrac{(1 + i)^n - 1}{i(1 + i)^n}$	Given P To find R $\dfrac{i(1 + i)^n}{(1 + i)^n - 1}$	n
1	1.030	0.9709	1.000	1.00000	0.971	1.03000	1
2	1.061	0.9426	2.030	0.49261	1.913	0.52261	2
3	1.093	0.9151	3.091	0.32353	2.829	0.35353	3
4	1.126	0.8885	4.184	0.23903	3.717	0.26903	4
5	1.159	0.8626	5.309	0.18835	4.580	0.21835	5
6	1.194	0.8375	6.468	0.15460	5.417	0.18460	6
7	1.230	0.8131	7.662	0.13051	6.230	0.16051	7
8	1.267	0.7894	8.892	0.11246	7.020	0.14246	8
9	1.305	0.7664	10.159	0.09843	7.786	0.12843	9
10	1.344	0.7441	11.464	0.08723	8.530	0.11723	10
11	1.384	0.7224	12.808	0.07808	9.253	0.10808	11
12	1.426	0.7014	14.192	0.07046	9.954	0.10046	12
13	1.469	0.6810	15.618	0.06403	10.635	0.09403	13
14	1.513	0.6611	17.086	0.05853	11.296	0.08853	14
15	1.558	0.6419	18.599	0.05377	11.938	0.08377	15
16	1.605	0.6232	20.157	0.04961	12.561	0.07961	16
17	1.653	0.6050	21.762	0.04595	13.166	0.07595	17
18	1.702	0.5874	23.414	0.04271	13.754	0.07271	18
19	1.754	0.5703	25.117	0.03981	14.324	0.06981	19
20	1.806	0.5537	26.870	0.03722	14.877	0.06722	20
21	1.860	0.5375	28.676	0.03487	15.415	0.06487	21
22	1.916	0.5219	30.537	0.03275	15.937	0.06275	22
23	1.974	0.5067	32.453	0.03081	16.444	0.06081	23
24	2.033	0.4919	34.426	0.02905	16.936	0.05905	24
25	2.094	0.4776	36.459	0.02743	17.413	0.05743	25
26	2.157	0.4637	38.553	0.02594	17.877	0.05594	26
27	2.221	0.4502	40.710	0.02456	18.327	0.05456	27
28	2.288	0.4371	42.931	0.02329	18.764	0.05329	28
29	2.357	0.4243	45.219	0.02211	19.188	0.05211	29
30	2.427	0.4120	47.575	0.02102	19.600	0.05102	30
31	2.500	0.4000	50.003	0.02000	20.000	0.05000	31
32	2.575	0.3883	52.503	0.01905	20.389	0.04905	32
33	2.652	0.3770	55.078	0.01816	20.766	0.04816	33
34	2.732	0.3660	57.730	0.01732	21.132	0.04732	34
35	2.814	0.3554	60.462	0.01654	21.487	0.04654	35
40	3.262	0.3066	75.401	0.01326	23.115	0.04326	40
45	3.782	0.2644	92.720	0.01079	24.519	0.04079	45
50	4.384	0.2281	112.797	0.00887	25.730	0.03887	50

3 Percent Interest

n	Given P To find S $(1+i)^n$	Given S To find P $\dfrac{1}{(1+i)^n}$	Given R To find S $\dfrac{(1+i)^n-1}{i}$	Given S To find R $\dfrac{i}{(1+i)^n-1}$	Given R To find P $\dfrac{(1+i)^n-1}{i(1+i)^n}$	Given P To find R $\dfrac{i(1+i)^n}{(1+i)^n-1}$	n
1	1.040	0.9615	1.000	1.00000	0.962	1.04000	1
2	1.082	0.9246	2.040	0.49020	1.886	0.53020	2
3	1.125	0.8890	3.122	0.32035	2.775	0.36035	3
4	1.170	0.8548	4.246	0.23549	3.630	0.27549	4
5	1.217	0.8219	5.416	0.18463	4.452	0.22463	5
6	1.265	0.7903	6.633	0.15076	5.242	0.19076	6
7	1.316	0.7599	7.898	0.12661	6.002	0.16661	7
8	1.369	0.7307	9.214	0.10853	6.733	0.14853	8
9	1.423	0.7026	10.583	0.09449	7.435	0.13449	9
10	1.480	0.6756	12.006	0.08329	8.111	0.12329	10
11	1.539	0.6496	13.486	0.07415	8.760	0.11415	11
12	1.601	0.6246	15.026	0.06655	9.385	0.10655	12
13	1.665	0.6006	16.627	0.06014	9.986	0.10014	13
14	1.732	0.5775	18.292	0.05467	10.563	0.09467	14
15	1.801	0.5553	20.024	0.04994	11.118	0.08994	15
16	1.873	0.5339	21.825	0.04582	11.652	0.08582	16
17	1.948	0.5134	23.698	0.04220	12.166	0.08220	17
18	2.026	0.4936	25.645	0.03899	12.659	0.07899	18
19	2.107	0.4746	27.671	0.03614	13.134	0.07614	19
20	2.191	0.4564	29.778	0.03358	13.590	0.07358	20
21	2.279	0.4388	31.969	0.03128	14.029	0.07128	21
22	2.370	0.4220	34.248	0.02920	14.451	0.06920	22
23	2.465	0.4057	36.618	0.02731	14.857	0.06731	23
24	2.563	0.3901	39.083	0.02559	15.247	0.06559	24
25	2.666	0.3751	41.646	0.02401	15.622	0.06401	25
26	2.772	0.3607	44.312	0.02257	15.983	0.06257	26
27	2.883	0.3468	47.084	0.02124	16.330	0.06124	27
28	2.999	0.3335	49.968	0.02001	16.663	0.06001	28
29	3.119	0.3207	52.966	0.01888	16.984	0.05888	29
30	3.243	0.3083	56.085	0.01783	17.292	0.05783	30
31	3.373	0.2965	59.328	0.01686	17.588	0.05686	31
32	3.508	0.2851	62.701	0.01595	17.874	0.05595	32
33	3.648	0.2741	66.210	0.01510	18.148	0.05510	33
34	3.794	0.2636	69.858	0.01431	18.411	0.05431	34
35	3.946	0.2534	73.652	0.01358	18.665	0.05358	35
40	4.801	0.2083	95.026	0.01052	19.793	0.05052	40
45	5.841	0.1712	121.029	0.00826	20.720	0.04826	45
50	7.107	0.1407	152.667	0.00655	21.482	0.04655	50

4 Percent Interest

n	Given P To find S $(1 + i)^n$	Given S To find P $\dfrac{1}{(1 + i)^n}$	Given R To find S $\dfrac{(1 + i)^n - 1}{i}$	Given S To find R $\dfrac{i}{(1 + i)^n - 1}$	Given R To find P $\dfrac{(1 + i)^n - 1}{i(1 + i)^n}$	Given P To find R $\dfrac{i(1 + i)^n}{(1 + i)^n - 1}$	n
1	1.050	0.9524	1.000	1.00000	0.952	1.05000	1
2	1.103	0.9070	2.050	0.48780	1.859	0.53780	2
3	1.158	0.8638	3.153	0.31721	2.723	0.36721	3
4	1.216	0.8227	4.310	0.23201	3.546	0.28201	4
5	1.276	0.7835	5.526	0.18097	4.329	0.23097	5
6	1.340	0.7462	6.802	0.14702	5.076	0.19702	6
7	1.407	0.7107	8.142	0.12282	5.786	0.17282	7
8	1.477	0.6768	9.549	0.10472	6.463	0.15472	8
9	1.551	0.6446	11.027	0.09069	7.108	0.14069	9
10	1.629	0.6139	12.57	0.07950	7.722	0.12950	10
11	1.710	0.5847	14.207	0.07039	8.306	0.12039	11
12	1.796	0.5568	15.917	0.06283	8.863	0.11283	12
13	1.886	0.5303	17.713	0.05646	9.394	0.10646	13
14	1.980	0.5051	19.599	0.05102	9.899	0.10102	14
15	2.079	0.4810	21.579	0.04634	10.380	0.09634	15
16	2.183	0.4581	23.657	0.04227	10.838	0.09227	16
17	2.292	0.4363	25.840	0.03870	11.274	0.08870	17
18	2.407	0.4155	28.132	0.03555	11.690	0.08555	18
19	2.527	0.3957	30.539	0.03275	12.085	0.08275	19
20	2.653	0.3769	33.066	0.03024	12.462	0.08024	20
21	2.786	0.3589	35.719	0.02800	12.821	0.07800	21
22	2.925	0.3418	38.505	0.02597	13.163	0.07597	22
23	3.072	0.3256	41.430	0.02414	13.489	0.07414	23
24	3.225	0.3101	44.502	0.02247	13.799	0.07247	24
25	3.386	0.2953	47.727	0.02095	14.094	0.07095	25
26	3.556	0.2812	51.113	0.01956	14.375	0.06956	26
27	3.733	0.2678	54.669	0.01829	14.643	0.06829	27
28	3.920	0.2551	58.403	0.01712	14.898	0.06712	28
29	4.116	0.2429	62.323	0.01605	15.141	0.06605	29
30	4.322	0.2314	66.439	0.01505	15.372	0.06505	30
31	4.538	0.2204	70.761	0.01413	15.593	0.06413	31
32	4.765	0.2099	75.299	0.01328	15.803	0.06328	32
33	5.003	0.1999	80.064	0.01249	16.003	0.06249	33
34	5.253	0.1904	85.067	0.01176	16.193	0.06176	34
35	5.516	0.1813	90.320	0.01107	16.374	0.06107	35
40	7.040	0.1420	120.800	0.00828	17.159	0.05828	40
45	8.985	0.1113	159.700	0.00626	17.774	0.05626	45
50	11.467	0.0872	209.348	0.00478	18.256	0.05478	50

5 Percent Interest

n	Given P To find S $(1 + i)^n$	Given S To find P $\dfrac{1}{(1 + i)^n}$	Given R To find S $\dfrac{(1 + i)^n - 1}{i}$	Given S To find R $\dfrac{i}{(1 + i)^n - 1}$	Given R To find P $\dfrac{(1 + i)^n - 1}{i(1 + i)^n}$	Given P To find R $\dfrac{i(1 + i)^n}{(1 + i)^n - 1}$	n
1	1.060	0.9434	1.000	1.00000	0.943	1.06000	1
2	1.124	0.8900	2.060	0.48544	1.833	0.54544	2
3	1.191	0.8396	3.184	0.31411	2.673	0.37411	3
4	1.262	0.7921	4.375	0.22859	3.465	0.28859	4
5	1.338	0.7473	5.637	0.17740	4.212	0.23740	5
6	1.419	0.7050	6.975	0.14336	4.917	0.20336	6
7	1.504	0.6651	8.394	0.11914	5.582	0.17914	7
8	1.594	0.6274	9.897	0.10104	6.210	0.16104	8
9	1.689	0.5919	11.491	0.08702	6.802	0.14702	9
10	1.791	0.5584	13.181	0.07587	7.360	0.13587	10
11	1.898	0.5268	14.972	0.06679	7.887	0.12679	11
12	2.012	0.4970	16.870	0.05928	8.384	0.11928	12
13	2.133	0.4688	18.882	0.05296	8.853	0.11296	13
14	2.261	0.4423	21.015	0.04758	9.295	0.10758	14
15	2.397	0.4173	23.276	0.04296	9.712	0.10296	15
16	2.540	0.3936	25.673	0.03895	10.106	0.09895	16
17	2.693	0.3714	28.213	0.03544	10.477	0.09544	17
18	2.854	0.3503	30.906	0.03236	10.828	0.09236	18
19	3.026	0.3305	33.760	0.02962	11.158	0.08962	19
20	3.207	0.3118	36.786	0.02718	11.470	0.08718	20
21	3.400	0.2942	39.993	0.02500	11.764	0.08500	21
22	3.604	0.2775	43.392	0.02305	12.042	0.08305	22
23	3.820	0.2618	46.996	0.02128	12.303	0.08128	23
24	4.049	0.2470	50.816	0.01968	12.550	0.07968	24
25	4.292	0.2330	54.865	0.01823	12.783	0.07823	25
26	4.549	0.2198	59.156	0.01690	13.003	0.07690	26
27	4.822	0.2074	63.706	0.01570	13.211	0.07570	27
28	5.112	0.1956	68.528	0.01459	13.406	0.07459	28
29	5.418	0.1846	73.640	0.01358	13.591	0.07358	29
30	5.743	0.1741	79.058	0.01265	13.765	0.07265	30
31	6.088	0.1643	84.802	0.01179	13.929	0.07179	31
32	6.453	0.1550	90.890	0.01100	14.084	0.07100	32
33	6.841	0.1462	97.343	0.01027	14.230	0.07027	33
34	7.251	0.1379	104.184	0.00960	14.368	0.06960	34
35	7.686	0.1301	111.435	0.00897	14.498	0.06897	35
40	10.286	0.0972	154.762	0.00646	15.046	0.06646	40
45	13.765	0.0727	212.744	0.00470	15.456	0.06470	45
50	18.420	0.0543	290.336	0.00344	15.762	0.06344	50

6 Percent Interest

n	Given P To find S $(1+i)^n$	Given S To find P $\dfrac{1}{(1+i)^n}$	Given R To find S $\dfrac{(1+i)^n-1}{i}$	Given S To find R $\dfrac{i}{(1+i)^n-1}$	Given R To find P $\dfrac{(1+i)^n-1}{i(1+i)^n}$	Given P To find R $\dfrac{i(1+i)^n}{(1+i)^n-1}$	n
1	1.070	0.9346	1.000	1.00000	0.935	1.07000	1
2	1.145	0.8734	2.070	0.48309	1.808	0.55309	2
3	1.225	0.8163	3.215	0.31105	2.624	0.38105	3
4	1.311	0.7629	4.440	0.22523	3.387	0.29523	4
5	1.403	0.7130	5.751	0.17389	4.100	0.24389	5
6	1.501	0.6663	7.153	0.13980	4.767	0.20980	6
7	1.606	0.6227	8.654	0.11555	5.389	0.18555	7
8	1.718	0.5820	10.260	0.09747	5.971	0.16747	8
9	1.838	0.5439	11.978	0.08349	6.515	0.15349	9
10	1.967	0.5083	13.816	0.07238	7.024	0.14238	10
11	2.105	0.4751	15.784	0.06336	7.499	0.13336	11
12	2.252	0.4440	17.888	0.05590	7.943	0.12590	12
13	2.410	0.4150	20.141	0.04965	8.358	0.11965	13
14	2.579	0.3878	22.550	0.04434	8.745	0.11434	14
15	2.759	0.3624	25.129	0.03979	9.108	0.10979	15
16	2.952	0.3387	27.888	0.03586	9.447	0.10586	16
17	3.159	0.3166	30.840	0.03243	9.763	0.10243	17
18	3.380	0.2959	33.999	0.02941	10.059	0.09941	18
19	3.617	0.2765	37.379	0.02675	10.336	0.09675	19
20	3.870	0.2584	40.995	0.02439	10.594	0.09439	20
21	4.141	0.2415	44.865	0.02229	10.836	0.09229	21
22	4.430	0.2257	49.006	0.02041	11.061	0.09041	22
23	4.741	0.2109	53.436	0.01871	11.272	0.08871	23
24	5.072	0.1971	58.177	0.01719	11.469	0.08719	24
25	5.427	0.1842	63.249	0.01581	11.654	0.08581	25
26	5.807	0.1722	68.676	0.01456	11.826	0.08456	26
27	6.214	0.1609	74.484	0.01343	11.987	0.08343	27
28	6.649	0.1504	80.698	0.01239	12.137	0.08239	28
29	7.114	0.1406	87.347	0.01145	12.278	0.08145	29
30	7.612	0.1314	94.461	0.01059	12.409	0.08059	30
31	8.145	0.1228	102.073	0.00980	12.532	0.07980	31
32	8.715	0.1147	110.218	0.00907	12.647	0.07907	32
33	9.325	0.1072	118.933	0.00841	12.754	0.07841	33
34	9.978	0.1002	128.259	0.00780	12.854	0.07780	34
35	10.677	0.0937	138.237	0.00723	12.948	0.07723	35
40	14.974	0.0668	199.635	0.00501	13.332	0.07501	40
45	21.002	0.0476	285.749	0.00350	13.606	0.07350	45
50	29.457	0.0339	406.529	0.00246	13.801	0.07246	50

7 Percent Interest

n	Given P To find S $(1+i)^n$	Given S To find P $\dfrac{1}{(1+i)^n}$	Given R To find S $\dfrac{(1+i)^n-1}{i}$	Given S To find R $\dfrac{i}{(1+i)^n-1}$	Given R To find P $\dfrac{(1+i)^n-1}{i(1+i)^n}$	Given P To find R $\dfrac{i(1+i)^n}{(1+i)^n-1}$	n
1	1.080	0.9259	1.000	1.00000	0.926	1.08000	1
2	1.166	0.8573	2.080	0.48077	1.783	0.56077	2
3	1.260	0.7938	3.246	0.30803	2.577	0.38803	3
4	1.360	0.7350	4.506	0.22192	3.312	0.30192	4
5	1.469	0.6806	5.867	0.17046	3.993	0.25046	5
6	1.587	0.6302	7.336	0.13632	4.623	0.21632	6
7	1.714	0.5835	8.923	0.11207	5.206	0.19207	7
8	1.851	0.5403	10.637	0.09401	5.747	0.17401	8
9	1.999	0.5002	12.488	0.08008	6.247	0.16008	9
10	2.159	0.4632	14.487	0.06903	6.710	0.14903	10
11	2.332	0.4289	16.645	0.06008	7.139	0.14008	11
12	2.518	0.3971	18.977	0.05270	7.536	0.13270	12
13	2.720	0.3677	21.495	0.04652	7.904	0.12652	13
14	2.937	0.3405	24.215	0.04130	8.244	0.12130	14
15	3.172	0.3152	27.152	0.03683	8.559	0.11683	15
16	3.426	0.2919	30.324	0.03298	8.851	0.11298	16
17	3.700	0.2703	33.750	0.02963	9.122	0.10963	17
18	3.996	0.2502	37.450	0.02670	9.372	0.10670	18
19	4.316	0.2317	41.446	0.02413	9.604	0.10413	19
20	4.661	0.2145	45.762	0.02185	9.818	0.10185	20
21	5.034	0.1987	50.423	0.01983	10.017	0.09983	21
22	5.437	0.1839	55.457	0.01803	10.201	0.09803	22
23	5.871	0.1703	60.893	0.01642	10.371	0.09642	23
24	6.341	0.1577	66.765	0.01498	10.529	0.09498	24
25	6.848	0.1460	73.106	0.01368	10.675	0.09368	25
26	7.396	0.1352	79.954	0.01251	10.810	0.09251	26
27	7.988	0.1252	87.351	0.01145	10.935	0.09145	27
28	8.627	0.1159	95.339	0.01049	11.051	0.09049	28
29	9.317	0.1073	103.966	0.00962	11.158	0.08962	29
30	10.063	0.0994	113.283	0.00883	11.258	0.08883	30
31	10.868	0.0920	123.346	0.00811	11.350	0.08811	31
32	11.737	0.0852	134.214	0.00745	11.435	0.08745	32
33	12.676	0.0789	145.951	0.00685	11.514	0.08685	33
34	13.690	0.0730	158.627	0.00630	11.587	0.08630	34
35	14.785	0.0676	172.317	0.00580	11.655	0.08580	35
40	21.725	0.0460	259.057	0.00386	11.925	0.08386	40
45	31.920	0.0313	386.506	0.00259	12.108	0.08259	45
50	46.902	0.0213	573.770	0.00174	12.233	0.08174	50

8 Percent Interest

n	Given P To find S $(1+i)^n$	Given S To find P $\dfrac{1}{(1+i)^n}$	Given R To find S $\dfrac{(1+i)^n-1}{i}$	Given S To find R $\dfrac{i}{(1+i)^n-1}$	Given R To find P $\dfrac{(1+i)^n-1}{i(1+i)^n}$	Given P To find R $\dfrac{i(1+i)^n}{(1+i)^n-1}$	n
1	1.100	0.9091	1.000	1.00000	0.909	1.10000	1
2	1.210	0.8264	2.100	0.47619	1.736	0.57619	2
3	1.331	0.7513	3.310	0.30211	2.487	0.40211	3
4	1.464	0.6830	4.641	0.21547	3.170	0.31547	4
5	1.611	0.6209	6.105	0.16380	3.791	0.26380	5
6	1.772	0.5645	7.716	0.12961	4.355	0.22961	6
7	1.949	0.5132	9.487	0.10541	4.868	0.20541	7
8	2.144	0.4665	11.436	0.08744	5.335	0.18744	8
9	2.358	0.4241	13.579	0.07364	5.759	0.17364	9
10	2.594	0.3855	15.937	0.06275	6.144	0.16275	10
11	2.853	0.3505	18.531	0.05396	6.495	0.15396	11
12	3.138	0.3186	21.384	0.04676	6.814	0.14676	12
13	3.452	0.2897	24.523	0.04078	7.103	0.14078	13
14	3.797	0.2633	27.975	0.03575	7.367	0.13575	14
15	4.177	0.2394	31.772	0.03147	7.606	0.13147	15
16	4.595	0.2176	35.950	0.02782	7.824	0.12782	16
17	5.054	0.1978	40.545	0.02466	8.022	0.12466	17
18	5.560	0.1799	45.599	0.02193	8.201	0.12193	18
19	6.116	0.1635	51.159	0.01955	8.365	0.11955	19
20	6.727	0.1486	57.275	0.01746	8.514	0.11746	20
21	7.400	0.1351	64.002	0.01562	8.649	0.11562	21
22	8.140	0.1228	71.403	0.01401	8.772	0.11401	22
23	8.954	0.1117	79.543	0.01257	8.883	0.11257	23
24	9.850	0.1015	88.497	0.01130	8.985	0.11130	24
25	10.835	0.0923	98.347	0.01017	9.077	0.11017	25
26	11.918	0.0839	109.182	0.00916	9.161	0.10916	26
27	13.110	0.0763	121.100	0.00826	9.237	0.10826	27
28	14.421	0.0693	134.210	0.00745	9.307	0.10745	28
29	15.863	0.0630	148.631	0.00673	9.370	0.10673	29
30	17.449	0.0573	164.494	0.00608	9.427	0.10608	30
31	19.194	0.0521	181.943	0.00550	9.479	0.10550	31
32	21.114	0.0474	201.138	0.00497	9.526	0.10497	32
33	23.225	0.0431	222.252	0.00450	9.569	0.10450	33
34	25.548	0.0391	245.477	0.00407	9.609	0.10407	34
35	28.102	0.0356	271.024	0.00369	9.644	0.10369	35
40	45.259	0.0221	442.593	0.00226	9.779	0.10226	40
45	72.890	0.0137	718.905	0.00139	9.863	0.10139	45
50	117.391	0.0085	1163.909	0.00086	9.915	0.10086	50

10 Percent Interest

n	i										n
	6%	8%	10%	12%	15%	20%	25%	30%	40%	50%	
1	1.06000	1.08000	1.10000	1.12000	1.15000	1.20000	1.25000	1.30000	1.40000	1.50000	1
2	0.54544	0.56077	0.57619	0.59170	0.61512	0.65455	0.69444	0.73478	0.81667	0.90000	2
3	0.37411	0.38803	0.40211	0.41635	0.43798	0.47473	0.51230	0.55063	0.62936	0.71053	3
4	0.28859	0.30192	0.31547	0.32923	0.35027	0.38629	0.42344	0.46163	0.54077	0.62308	4
5	0.23740	0.25046	0.26380	0.27741	0.29832	0.33438	0.37184	0.41058	0.49136	0.57582	5
6	0.20336	0.21632	0.22961	0.24323	0.26424	0.30071	0.33882	0.37840	0.46126	0.54812	6
7	0.17914	0.19207	0.20541	0.21912	0.24036	0.27742	0.31634	0.35687	9.44192	0.53108	7
8	0.16104	0.17401	0.18744	0.20130	0.22285	0.26061	0.30040	0.34191	0.42804	0.52030	8
9	0.14702	0.16008	0.17364	0.18768	0.20957	0.24808	0.28876	0.33123	0.42034	0.51335	9
10	0.13587	0.14903	0.16275	0.17698	0.19925	0.23852	0.28007	0.32346	0.41432	0.50823	10
11	0.12679	0.14008	0.15396	0.16842	0.19107	0.23110	0.27349	0.31773	0.41013	0.50585	11
12	0.11928	0.13270	0.14676	0.16144	0.18448	0.22526	0.26845	0.31345	0.40718	0.50388	12
13	0.11296	0.12652	0.14078	0.15568	0.17911	0.22062	0.26454	0.31024	0.40510	0.50258	13
14	0.10758	0.12130	0.13575	0.15087	0.17469	0.21689	0.26150	0.30782	0.40363	0.50172	14
15	0.10296	0.11683	0.13147	0.14682	0.17102	0.21388	0.25912	0.30598	0.40259	0.50114	15
16	0.09895	0.11298	0.12782	0.14339	0.16795	0.21144	0.25724	0.30458	0.40185	0.50076	16
17	0.09544	0.10963	0.12466	0.14046	0.16537	0.20944	0.25576	0.30351	0.40132	0.50051	17
18	0.09236	0.10670	0.12193	0.13794	0.16319	0.20781	0.25459	0.30269	0.40094	0.50034	18
19	0.08962	0.10413	0.11955	0.13576	0.16134	0.20646	0.25366	0.30206	0.40067	0.50023	19
20	0.08718	0.10185	0.11746	0.13388	0.15976	0.20536	0.25292	0.30159	0.40048	0.50016	20
25	0.07823	0.09368	0.11017	0.12750	0.15470	0.20212	0.25095	0.30043	0.40009	0.50002	25
30	0.07265	0.08883	0.10608	0.12414	0.15230	0.20085	0.25031	0.30011	0.40002	0.50000	30
40	0.06646	0.08386	0.10226	0.12130	0.15056	0.20014	0.25003	0.30008	0.40001	0.50000	40
50	0.06344	0.08174	0.10086	0.12042	0.15014	0.20002	0.25000	0.30001	0.40000	0.50000	50
100	0.06018	0.08004	0.10001	0.12000	0.15000	0.20000	0.25000	0.30000	0.40000	0.50000	100

$$\frac{i(1 + i)^n}{(1 + i)^n - 1}$$ **For Interest Rates from 6 to 50 Percent Given *P*, to Find *R***

INDEX

A

Accuracy, 30
Adaptive information systems, 29–30
Assumed certainty, 87
Autonomous investment, 81
Average cost, 56–79

B

Basic contract, 35–36
Batch budgeting, 100
Bias, 30
Borrowed funds, 4

C

Capital
  allocation, 51–52
  cost of, 50
  rationing, 48–50
  recovery, 9
Cash flow, 2–3
Centralization, 103–10
Communication, 100
Complimentarities, 102–3
Consistent decision, 38
Continuous budgeting, 101
Coordination, 103
Cost of capital, 50

D

Decentralization, 103–10
Delegation, 105–10
Depreciation, 17–19
Diversification, 46, 52–54

E

Economic service life, 58–61
Equal service lives, 13–14
Equivalent annual cost principle, 11–12
Estimating, 29–30
Evaluation, 99–100
Expansion, 56, 82–83
Expected profit principle, 33, 44–46

F

Fixed percentage depreciation, 18–19
Forecasts, 29–30
Futurity, 2–3

G

Gate value, 108–10
General replacement model, 77–78

I

Indivisibility of assets, 84–85
Induced investment, 81–82
Interest
  basic uses, 3–7
  formulas, 5–7
  monthly, 7
  tax aspects, 21–22
Investment
  autonomous, 81–85
  induced, 81–82
  programs, 48
  recovery, 9

L

Leasing, 16–17
Linear projections, 84

M

Machine selection, 7
Maintenance of capacity, 56–79
Management information systems, 25–26

N

New product demand, 85

O

Obsolescence, 65–77
Opportunity costs, 4–5

P

Planning
  horizon, 62
  long range, 1–2

This book has been set in 10 and 9 point Caledonia, leaded 2 points. Chapter numbers are in 14 point Venus Medium Extended; chapter titles are in 16 point Venus Medium Extended. The size of the type page is 27 by 46½ picas.